Dave's Subs

A Novel Story about Workplace Accountability

David Marx

By Your Side Studios

Dave's Subs

By Your Side Studios
5048 Tennyson Parkway, Suite 250
Plano, TX 75024
WWW.BYYOURSIDESTUDIOS.COM
WWW.DAVESSUBS.COM

Pre-Publication Edition

Marx, David
Dave's Subs

ISBN 978-0-9840419-6-1

AT HIS BEST, MAN IS THE NOBLEST OF ALL ANIMALS

ARISTOTLE

For those who assume the responsibility
to stand in judgment of others

Table of Contents

THE STORY

THE DAY IT HAPPENED

IT NEVER OCCURRED TO MILO,
THAT SOMEDAY,
HE WOULD MAKE THE EVENING NEWS.

Milo had been working for Dave's Subs at its original location, mentored by the chain's founder, Dave Adams, for just under three years. Milo was a good employee, productive and well liked by Dave's customers. He was so good that Dave tapped him to open and manage the chain's sixth store. Milo's journey as a manager began well. For a store opening, it was pretty smooth sailing, until a lunch rush about a month into business.

Patti Foster is the managing partner in a powerful law firm, Lawrence, Foster and Sepulveda, in the downtown office building where Milo's location of Dave's Subs is located. Patti is an

1

experienced and successful plaintiff's attorney specializing in suing, on behalf of her clients, doctors accused of medical malpractice. Patti is a neat freak, totally organized in everything she does — she is someone, as they say, who likes her ducks in a row. She's great at her job, as her law firm's billboards around town attest. She has one child, now a grown daughter. From all appearances, Patti's only handicap in life is that she suffers from a severe form of celiac disease, making her extremely intolerant of gluten, a protein found in wheat, rye and barley, i.e., most bread. She runs marathons, she's on the board of the city's ballet, and she champions the causes of clients who are hurt by negligent doctors. She's on top of her game in everything she does. She just has celiac disease.

For the 1 in 100 people who suffer from celiac disease, avoiding gluten is serious business. Not only are there the immediate effects from the body mounting an immune response from ingesting gluten (think vomiting and extreme abdominal pain), there are potential long-term health effects including damage to the small intestine, development of other autoimmune diseases such as multiple sclerosis, infertility and miscarriage, neurological conditions, and finally, intestinal cancers. Ingesting even small amounts of gluten, as small as crumbs left on a cutting board, can be enough to trigger an immune response. It's bad stuff, and there is no cure. The only treatment for celiac disease is avoiding gluten.

On a warm spring day in April, with the store open a little over a month, Patti decided to try out Dave's Subs. She'd heard from a colleague that they offered gluten-free rolls. She'd spent an intense morning deposing a very confrontational defendant in a medical malpractice claim. She was thinking ahead to Friday when she had a flight booked to Honolulu to attend her daughter's wedding. She was exhausted, irritable, hungry, and in a rush. And right there on the ground floor of her building, a tall shiny monument to the city's vibrant business center, sat Dave's Subs, a new shop, full of the promise of great food (and gluten-free rolls!) offered with fast and friendly service. Her partners had raved, and today was the day she would give it a try.

Alisha Fontaine is a sub "artisan" at Dave's Subs. On this day, Alisha was Patti's artisan. Patti ordered the house specialty, a club sandwich piled high with roast beef, turkey, and bacon strips, a few slices of cheddar cheese, tomatoes, green peppers and mayonnaise, all on a gluten-free roll. Patti checked her phone for email and text messages while Alisha went to the bread storage next to the oven to grab a gluten-free roll. She reached up to the single highest rack of the roll warmer where the morning bread delivery guy would have placed the gluten-free rolls.

On this particular day, Milo was out of the shop. For the first time, Alisha was acting as both manager and artisan. It was, so far, a very busy day and Alisha, like Patti, felt rushed and frazzled. As Alisha walked the 10 feet to the bread rack to grab the gluten-free bread, she noticed Fred Simpson, another sub artisan, motioning her to come over to his workstation. Her eyes shifted from Fred to his obviously irritated customer.

Now wearing her manager's hat, she wondered what was happening with Fred's customer. Reaching the bread rack, Alisha grabbed a roll from the top rack. Alisha didn't look at the bread; her eyes were instead firmly fixed on Fred's increasingly agitated customer who was, by this time, waving his pointed finger at Fred.

Clearly something was not going right with Fred's customer; Fred's frantic motioning to Alisha was evidence that his problem had become hers.

Back to the roll. By corporate policy, Alisha was supposed to hold up the roll upon retrieving it, and call out "I have gluten-free!" whereupon a fellow artisan would look at the gluten-free roll, distinguishable by the crosshatch pattern on its freshly baked top, and say "You've got gluten-free!" This was the safety check to ensure no single human mistake would result in a customer improperly receiving a regular roll made with gluten – poison to those with celiac disease.

On this fate-filled day, the gluten-free rolls were improperly stocked. The usual deliveryman was on vacation and his replacement had not yet covered this route. Delivering the bread an hour later than usual due to a scheduling mix-up with his truck, the deliveryman knew that gluten-free rolls needed to be segregated from the other rolls, but did not know how they were to be segregated at Dave's Subs.

He looked for someone to ask about how the bread should be placed in the rack. He could see the sub artisans were knee deep in slicing and dicing in preparation for the day's rush. One of the things that drew him to this delivery job was the solitary comfort of driving the truck; once he learned a route, and customer orders, his job required little direct interaction with actual human beings throughout the day. A little shy and now more than a little frazzled himself by the delays and the new route, and with an hour to make up from the scheduling snafu, he put the gluten-free rolls on the bottom rack rather than interrupt the artisans in their food prep.

For him the lack of certainty about where to put the rollss caused little stress, given the gluten-free rolls were clearly distinguishable by their unique crosshatch pattern. If they were in the wrong place, any sub artisan would notice as they were grabbing the roll, or surely at the point they sliced the roll to make the sandwich. With a shy smile and a wave to the sub artisans, he was on his way to his next delivery.

Milo normally receives the bread order before the artisans arrive for their day. Milo checks every morning that the breads are properly stocked, whole wheat on the bottom shelves, the big stash of regular white in the middle, and the special, gluten-free rolls on the top rack. Consistency in stocking the breads improves speed and efficiency for the sub artisans and helps to keep spilled food costs low. Alisha, briefed on the pre-opening prep duties, and having actually worked one pre-opening shift with Milo, was nonetheless unaware that Milo checked the bread orders upon intake. In Milo's quick briefing to his high performing artisan, Milo forgot to share that he personally checked the arrangement of sub rolls. And for the crew of five artisans, it was simply something they took for granted – the rolls were always arranged in the same order, whether it was done by the bread deliveryman, by Milo, or by the gods, the sub artisans gave it no thought.

As Alisha turned from the bread rack, she did not call out "I've got gluten-free!" The need to do the check was somewhere in her mind. She'd done it many times in her short tenure at Dave's, and she knew it when interviewed after the event. It was there in her brain, it just wasn't in her conscious thought at that moment. Instead, as she walked back to her workstation, she was focusing with her full conscious brain on the ordeal unfolding at Fred's workstation. Whatever was happening between Fred and his customer, it was not good.

As she prepared Patti's sub, as she assembled the turkey club, she did not notice the missing crosshatch pattern on the top of her sub roll. It was there for a reason, offered up by the bread vendor as a special safety feature, the unique pattern on the bread that would keep unsuspecting customers from getting the wrong bread. And it generally worked. Every sub artisan could tell of times they caught themselves merely by recognition of that familiar crosshatch on the top of the roll. It was unique and without question identifiable.

Yet, for whatever reason, it appeared that Alisha did not pick up on the crosshatch cue. She did not realize she was using a normal roll. She did not realize the hazard she was creating. What she was thinking about, and what she was aware of, was Fred's irate customer. To get to Fred and his customer, time was of the essence, and a focused Alisha pushed through her sub-making task while thinking of her impending approach to Fred's customer. In a blink, Patti was off with a bottle of lemon-infused sparkling water and her poisonous turkey club sandwich, a first time Dave's Subs guest with no way of knowing that the roll she carried away was not the gluten-free bread she so specifically ordered.

A late bread delivery. A new driver. An improperly stocked bread rack. A first time customer. An employee's first foray into covering as manager on duty. An irate customer requiring attention. An instinctive reach to a familiar place to find the roll she was looking for. A failure to confirm the roll was gluten-free.

Not noticing the crosshatch pattern was missing. It was a series of mostly unremarkable events. No evil actor. No intention to harm.

Yet, that was all it took. Within 30 minutes, Patti Foster was on her way to a severe reaction. And it took her only those 30 minutes to know what was wrong. Patti had felt the symptoms before. She knew immediately that there had been a mistake. Within the hour, a colleague was taking her to the emergency room of the very hospital where she had deposed the accused doctor earlier in the day. Within 90 minutes, the diagnosis was confirmed – an adverse reaction to gluten. She would spend three days in the hospital. And she would miss that flight to Hawaii for her only child's wedding.

Patti, the consummate attorney, threatened to file suit against Dave's Subs while still in the hospital. She even granted a hospital bed interview to a good friend, an investigative reporter, at a local TV evening news program just prior to her discharge. She shared with the world the dangers of visiting Dave's Subs and the general dangers of improper food handling. The interview seemed part accusations levied at Dave's Subs, part trolling for prospective clients injured by restaurant foul ups. In either side of the story, Patti Foster was clearly incensed and appeared out for blood.

Dave's Subs had let her down; they had breached the duty of the public trust that dining out would not land you in the hospital for three days. Perhaps protecting her interest in Dave's Subs ability to pay out a settlement in the lawsuit she was filing, she fell short of calling for Dave's Sub's to be shut down. She did, however, want Alisha's head, telling both print and media outlets, "If Dave's Sub's is committed to delivering a safe product, then that woman, my server, should be fired. Dave's Subs cannot afford to keep on its staff an unsafe employee who is so clearly a threat to our community."

Six years earlier, before the Patti Foster event, Dave Adams was a securities trader on Wall Street. He was pretty successful at what he did. He put in long hours, commuting to Manhattan each day from his home in suburban New Jersey. It was a high stakes environment. His securities firm churned through young traders like they were raw meat. Into the grinder as whole human beings, churned out as indistinguishable links of trader sausage. For Dave, each day was a roll of the dice. Each day a chance that he'd make the big deal, or make the big mistake and be sent home, another trader who was only as good as his last trade.

For the most part, Dave had enjoyed the intensity and high stakes of trading, but now with a wife and two young sons, the uncertainty was more than he could handle, more than he wanted to put upon his family. The inherent risk of making a poor trade costing his client or firm nearly unfathomable amounts of money, the vagaries of an economy far outside his control – these posed more risk and uncertainty than he was willing to accept.

So, six years ago, in a final high-stakes move, Dave Adams emptied his 401K to open Dave's Subs. Dave appreciated the risk of opening a sandwich shop; his fellow traders mostly looked dumbfounded when he asked them what they thought of his idea – "are you kidding me" being one of the kinder and more supportive responses from his colleagues. Dave was good at running the numbers, calculating his potential return on investment. He knew he would be replacing the known stresses of trading with all the unknown stresses of being a small business owner, but the intangibles favored leaving Wall Street.

Dave cut his commute from an hour or more each way depending on delays on the train to less than 15 minutes on a busy traffic day. He was home for dinner most nights and could actually contemplate the possibility of coaching his sons' Little League teams when they were old enough to play. His attention to detail, his insistence on beginning with high quality, locally sourced (when possible) ingredients, and his knack for developing quality employees happy to work part time while pursuing other life passions, resulted in rapid expansion for Dave's Subs – a new location roughly every year. Life was good. Dave felt in control of his own destiny. That is until that warm April afternoon.

Dave, Milo, and the entire team at Milo's store were devastated by the Patti Foster event. They felt awful about the harm to Patti; they were, however, becoming angry at Patti's continued public condemnation of the store. Dealing with Patti was Dave's first priority. All he wanted was to silence his once customer now turned adversary. Dave quickly settled for $75,000, with Patti agreeing to stop her public outcry and forfeit any potential litigation. Dave knew the longer Patti Foster was allowed to campaign against his store, the harder it would be for Dave's Subs to recover.

The focus was necessarily on Patti Foster, which left Alisha in purgatory. Would she be fired? When would she be fired? Her peers at Milo's store were particularly interested to know. And Milo's employees were not the only ones curious about what would happen with Alisha; across the Dave's Subs operation, employees watched.

Many were of the mindset "there but for the grace of God, go I" as it related to inadvertently grabbing the wrong bread roll. Particularly sympathetic were the artisans who worked with Alisha and were beneficiaries of her sunny disposition and willingness to step in and help where needed. Others, however, wanted Alisha gone. In their mind, she was a threat to Dave's Subs, and by association, a threat to their own jobs. Alisha screwed up; she sent a customer to the hospital through her screw-up and that had resulted in really bad press for them. Business was down. Alisha needed to go.

Dave and Milo were in constant communication in the aftermath of Alisha's mishap. Once they extinguished the Patti Foster fire, they turned their attention to Alisha. To give themselves some breathing room they put Alisha on two weeks of paid administrative leave. Dave sought counsel from some of his Wall Street friends, those of the "you're only as good as your last trade" mindset, from new friends he'd met in the small business community, and from his own legal counsel. They were fairly universal in their advice; Alisha was just unsafe to have around, she was a detriment to the business. Satisfy the masses' thirst for blood, throw Alisha to the wolves, let the public devour her, and watch them quickly forget about this public relations debacle, that was pretty much the consensus.

But these people did not know Alisha like Dave and Milo knew Alisha, or as her coworkers knew her. They only saw her through Patti Foster's and the media's eyes – a sub artisan who made the mistake that endangered the life of a customer. For Dave, the advice brought back memories of his days on Wall Street, only now the mantra ringing in his ears was "you're only as good as your last sandwich." Starting his own business did indeed bring him a measure of job security, yet one mistake was now putting one of his employees – and potentially his business - on the chopping block.

With the settlement behind him, and with Alisha approaching the end of her two weeks of administrative leave, Dave and Milo were still struggling with what to do. It just didn't seem fair to either one of them to define Alisha by this one mishap, this one sandwich, regardless of how dire and costly the consequences. It was also clear that Milo really did not want to play hatchet man in this scenario. He could fire an underperforming employee or somebody who seemed to have too much fun on weekends to actually make it to her substation on time on Monday morning, but this was different. This was big. And neither Dave nor Milo felt ready to cast that first stone.

Decision Time

Dave lived in a more rural part of New Jersey. The 1970's split-level he shared with his wife and two sons sat at the end of a cul-de-sac, shaded by old walnut and elm trees. It had been a rough two weeks on the home front. Dave was melancholy, a little short with his two young sons and with his wife who needed him to take over after she'd been with them all day. Instead, Dave holed up in his home office, staring out the window at his grass getting longer and longer, thinking to himself, "This is not why I left Wall Street." Dave was not feeling much grief over the $75,000 settlement. That was only money, and given it was Dave's Subs that caused the harm, Dave had no real angst about the payout. That was a cost of doing business. It was Alisha who was causing Dave's heavy heart.

The best part of the house for Dave was his office, with its huge windows giving him a wonderful view of his deep green lawn as it faded into the densely packed line of sugar maples along the back fence. It was here, in his office, that Dave had spent nearly two weeks brooding over the event, his eyes moving around the walls, randomly lighting on framed sports memorabilia, goofy family photos, his diplomas. A small but elegant frame kept drawing his attention; in it was a quote from a Martin Luther King speech he gave in opposition to America's part in the Vietnam War:

> "THERE COMES A TIME WHEN ONE MUST TAKE A POSITION THAT IS NEITHER SAFE, NOR POLITIC, NOR POPULAR, BUT HE MUST TAKE IT BECAUSE CONSCIENCE TELLS HIM IT IS RIGHT."
>
> *MARTIN LUTHER KING – FEBRUARY 6, 1968*

Dave's mother had given it to him at Dave's Subs' Grand Opening six years ago. As Dave unwrapped the gift, she added the advice she'd given him and his siblings throughout his childhood, "Be a part of the change, sweetie."

Dave's parents, Gus and Joan, lived outside Baltimore, his father a professor of American history, his mother a civil rights attorney in the U.S. Department of Justice. Dave suspected that from his parents perspective, neither his days as a securities trader nor his success with Dave's Subs lived up to their aspirations for him. Certainly, they were proud of him. Dave knew that. But he'd grown up with parents who pushed him to think beyond himself. "Be the change you wish to see in the world," they would always say, quoting Mahatma Gandhi. For Dave, in his mid-thirties, he had yet to find the change he wished to see, the change he wished to be. Until now.

When his mom had given Dave the advice along with the framed quote, he knew what she meant. As a civil rights attorney, Dave's mom had spent much of her life advocating for change. Joan was growing older, and increasingly tired as an attorney for the Department of Justice. Her gift to her son was essentially passing the baton – a hope that somehow her son Dave would continue the fight to help make the world a better place. And Dave knew the history of King's quote – Dr. King was being challenged by his peers to align his position on the war with that of the then current Administration so as not to harm the progress of the civil rights movement. Dave's mother knew that his time would come, as it does for everyone, when he would have to take a position in a time of challenge and controversy.

Dave thought about the very real harm Dave's Subs, through Alisha's hand, had inflicted on Patti. He thought about Alisha, a good employee, but whose error had caused him and Dave's Subs real harm. Dave had been staring at the Kennedy quote for the past two weeks. It was beautiful. Yet nothing in this lofty quote gave him guidance in this situation. If he fired Alisha, it wouldn't be for the traditional concerns of the civil rights movement - her gender, her religious preferences, or for the color of her skin. He was not embroiled in the civil rights movement – and this was not a civil rights issue, at least not yet.

Yet, those words from his trading days, "You're only as good as your last trade," continued to ring through his head. "This is not about who Alisha is; it's about what Alisha did," he thought to himself.

But what precisely had Alisha *done?* While she had no doubt caused a lot of harm to Patti Foster and to Dave's Subs, what she'd done, both Dave and Milo agreed, was commit a human error.

Alisha did not *intend* the harm to Patti or to Dave's Subs, nor did she *intend* to skip the safety step. Inadvertency ran throughout her conduct. Alisha had made a mistake and that, for Dave, was as much an immutable human characteristic as the color of Alisha's eyes. Dave kept pushing his thinking – was recognizing human fallibility another civil rights issue?

"Look," Dave had said to Milo during one of their many meetings over the past two weeks, "Patti's event was the product of what we all share, an inescapable human fallibility. There were so many things that contributed to Alisha making the error on that day. If 'to err is human' how can I in good conscience fire her for that? Fire her for being human?" It was for Dave more of the same, the "you're only as good as your last trade" approach. Dave had left his job on Wall Street to get away from that philosophy. Perhaps this was the place where Dave could live out his mother's hope for her children to "be the change in the world you want to see."

Dave turned to his laptop and began to write. He would challenge the wisdom of his Wall Street friends, his fellow small business owners, and even his attorney. When he was done, Dave had written the following letter to his employees.

TO THE EMPLOYEES OF DAVE'S SUBS

As a company, we have faced a difficult time the past few weeks. An event occurred that caused significant harm to one of our valued customers, which in turn damaged the reputation and good will of Dave's Subs.

The employee involved in this event has been a loyal, dedicated, and hardworking team member. I know that this employee did not intend to cause the harm; she committed what each of us is prone to do on a daily basis – she made a mistake.

I have received a steady stream of inputs, some quite loud, demanding that this employee be held accountable, from the customer we harmed, to media, to our legal counsel; it being understood, of course, that to be held accountable means our employee must be fired.

For what reason should this employee be fired? For what is she accountable? For an admittedly bad outcome? For the mistake? For both? Are any of us immune to either making a mistake or from the potentially bad outcomes arising from that human mistake? I don't think we are.

I believe the demand for earthly perfection is unrealistic, and simply unfair. As an employer, I choose to recognize that we are all only human, that we will, in fact, make mistakes, some with grave consequences and some with little to no consequences. Like the color of our eyes, our human fallibility is an immutable characteristic of being human. As a result, I will not fire an employee simply because they have made a human mistake. We will instead simply strive to help each and every team member be as successful as they can be given their natural talents, and the willingness to apply those talents at Dave's Subs. With this behind us, let's all get back to what makes us Dave's Subs – good food, fast and friendly service,

Dave

It was a bold statement of principle. At least at Dave's Subs, perfection would not be the standard. Employees would be held accountable, not through the press or an angry customer, but through a single principle that we as humans could not be perfect. It was a vision for how Dave's Subs would treat its employees, how they would be managed throughout the day. For Dave, it was not about giving up on what humans could achieve – but instead looking for more effective ways to produce better outcomes. Expecting perfection was not going to get us far, as Dave could see it. And, it was simply unjust.

Dave's letter was about to send Milo on a journey to understand just what it meant to be accountable at work - a journey in pursuit of a workable system of workplace justice. Milo listened intently to what Dave said to him, "Well, we're committed now. We're not going to fire an employee simply because they made a mistake. Now you, Milo, have to operationalize it. We feel pretty strongly that we are conceptually right; we've got the right vision. Now we just have to make it work in practice. I'm putting this on you to figure it out, to make this work."

Milo had a sense that Dave's letter oversimplified the matter, and in fact, oversimplified what happened in Alisha's event. Yet, Dave had made a statement of principle, and in concept, Milo agreed. Perfection should not be the expectation. People – employees – would make mistakes. Now it was in Milo's lap to make it work. First task, inform his team of Alisha's status.

The store had been open less than two months. During those first two months, if Milo needed to communicate with his team, it happened before the store opened. With just five part time employees, once the store opened, there had never really been a need for staff meetings. Yet, Dave's letter gave Milo reason to break with tradition and call the crew in early for a staff meeting – one that would, rightly or wrongly, occur without Alisha. The next day, she would be at work, having finished her two weeks of administrative leave. In the eyes of Milo's team, this particular process had dragged on. The team only knew that Alisha had been put on paid leave. For everyone, it was time for a resolution.

Milo's store is the newest location of Dave's Subs, having served its first customers in early March. It's officially called Store #6. The store is located in a relatively small space on the ground floor of an upscale office tower, limited in its current location to four artisan workstations. It has seating for 28 people within the store, with seating for another 16 outside, weather permitting. Dave has set up his business like a bank – the task for each sandwich artisan to provide great service to customers, one at a time. There is no assembly line. Dave's Subs accepts only credit and debit cards – even with the bank fees associated with accepting credit cards, the delay in waiting for someone to dig the exact change out of the bottom of their pants pocket or purse is costlier still.

Customers wait in line for an artisan, she or he makes the food to order, swipes a credit card and they're off. No soda machine - too messy, the carbonization takes too long to change, the syrup needs to be replaced, and it creates a bottle neck near the seating area - only bottled juices and naturally flavored waters. It's an extremely fast paced environment during the standard business lunch hours from 11:30 – 1:00, when each artisan will produce on average 40 subs an hour – all while developing a personal rapport with customers to garner their loyal, repeat business.

Milo, as manager, holds the only salaried position. He does the local accounting, purchasing, and marketing. When the store is open, he does food prep for the four artisan stations. He's in by 7:00 and leaves around 5:00.

The five artisans work a staggered schedule. They work either an opening shift from 9:00 am – 2:00 pm, or closing shift from 10:30 am – 3:30 pm. Four artisans work on each day. When no one is on vacation, each artisan gets roughly four shifts per week (20 hours). Artisans receive no paid benefits – no health insurance, no paid vacation, no paid sick leave. It's a simple employment model – come to work and get paid. Don't come to work, don't get paid. Starting hourly wages are 25% above minimum wage.

As a team, Milo's location had been doing great. Prior to Patti's event, it was already a profitable store for Dave, providing good food, with fast and friendly service to its downtown customers. Dave's strategy of using locally grown foods prepared by friendly sub artisans was playing well with the younger, hip clientele. The store's sales had grown briskly, in part from the good reputation created by Dave's five other stores. Milo's store was already feeling the strain of its success, with customer feedback consistently rating wait times as "needs improvement" as Dave's Subs' popularity increased. During the peak load time, around noon, the average wait time was pushing 15 minutes.

Milo himself is 34 years old. His team sees Milo as customer focused, with strong attention to detail. "Remember, good food, fast and friendly service – make it so," was the call to action Milo would announce ahead of each shift, mimicking Captain Jean Luc Picard of the starship Enterprise.

If Fred Simpson was working that day, he'd quip, "Aye aye, Captain," in response. Fred's name was certainly apropos; he seemed more like a character from *The Simpsons* than a real life human being. Twenty-six years old and still single, Fred was openly on the hunt for a wife, and he made sure everyone knew it. The jokester among the group, there was nothing Fred enjoyed more than a good, deep-belly laugh – except perhaps, causing one of his co-workers to break out in uncontrollable laughter over Fred's antics.

Every one of Dave's artisans had an open, cheery disposition, even Charles, a 66-year-old retired schoolteacher. He'd taken the job at Dave's to give his wife a break by getting out of the house a bit, and to supplement his retirement income. Charles kept himself young at heart, in part by playing on-line games like *Halo*, and by creating websites for friends and family. Charles was, for Milo, a wonder. Nearly twice his age, Milo knew he had much to learn from Charles. Whether it was his age or his having been a schoolteacher, patience, kindness and wisdom just seemed to flow from Charles.

Esther was at the other end of the spectrum, an energetic 22 year old. She'd been living at home while pursuing a paramedic certificate through an evening program at her local community college. She also had a second job as a Pilates instructor at a neighborhood fitness center. Esther was a bit of a tomboy. When she wasn't at work or school, she was either helping her father restore an old 1967 Ford Mustang or out at the track racing motorcycles. Extremely competitive, Esther made it clear by her actions that no one was going to make subs faster than her. The lunch rush was a sprint and Esther played to win.

Bryce was the last of the artisans, showing up a few minutes late to the staff meeting. Bryce was one of the lost boys of the Sudan who immigrated to the U.S. when orphaned by the Sudanese

Civil War. He was, understandably, a cautious man; uncertainty made him anxious. He, more than any of the other artisans, wanted to know what the rules were, what the expectations were, and what happened when people didn't meet those. The uncertainty of the aftermath of Alisha's event hit Bryce the hardest. Milo wasn't sure if it was the harm to Patti, the potential impact on Dave's Subs (and by extension, on Bryce's job), or what was going to happen to Alisha that bothered him the most. Either way, Bryce was visibly anxious.

The four artisans had been called in 15 minutes early. Since Alisha was on administrative leave, everyone had worked every day since the Patti Foster event. In general, they had been hopeful when they saw that Alisha had been put on administrative leave rather than summarily fired. They took it as further proof that Alisha at least had a hope of remaining at Dave's Subs when they saw that no advertisement was placed for another artisan. For them, this was all good news, as they liked Alisha. She was a high performer, and an enjoyable person to work with. The meeting, with Alisha absent, had raised anxiety again - would Alisha be returning to Dave's Subs?

Milo started the meeting somberly, "I'm sure you can all guess why we're here."

"It's Alisha," responded Fred.

"You fired her," said Bryce.

"No," said Milo, "We have not." Milo then reached into the folder in his hand and pulled out four copies of Dave's letter. He handed them out to his team. Milo sat quietly while his team read, with varying degrees of anxiety and skepticism.

"When does she come back?" asked Esther, looking up from her copy.

"Tomorrow. I spoke with her earlier today," replied Milo.

Charles looked the most shocked of them all. Milo looked right at him. "What are you thinking?" he asked Charles.

"It's not how the world works," said Charles. "Until I read this letter, I thought for sure Alisha was gone. In the real world, when someone screws up like Alisha did, they get fired. Why take this risk? I mean, I like Alisha just as much as everybody else does. But why take this risk with public perception already against us? I think most people will figure if the one who made the customer sick is gone, then it's safe to get a sub from us again."

"Dave simply wanted to do the right thing," Milo said, unable to hide his own skepticism and uncertainty about the practical application of Dave's letter. "We'll have to see how it plays out," Milo admitted. "Now, let's get to work. Alisha said she would stop by this afternoon. Let's all welcome her back."

For the most part, Milo and his team were relieved. The past two weeks had been hard on them all. Alisha was coming back. And hopefully, their lunchtime lines would return. For all of them, a 15-minute wait was looking like a good thing. They all wanted things to be back to where they were just a few weeks before.

Not So Easy

His team thought it was goofy. Raise the bread roll and say, "I've got gluten-free." For Milo, hiring on at Dave's original store, it was just part of the deal. His fellow artisans were doing the safety check. He just went along with the crowd. For Milo's store it was different. Alisha, Bryce, Charles, Esther, and Fred all started together as new employees. It was up to Milo to teach them what their jobs required, including that seemingly goofy safety check. And it was not enough that he taught his team the rules, it was up to Milo to build a culture that promoted and reinforced doing the check.

It had been bothering Milo for some time. Prior to Alisha's event, he had seen his team sometimes skipping the check. Was it by choice? Milo didn't know. Yet every time he saw it skipped, he would call it out. "Fred, don't forget the check. Call out that you have a gluten-free roll." Milo knew quite well that Patti Foster's event was not the first time that the check had been skipped at his store. Would his team, in the middle of the lunchtime rush, sometimes forget? Yes. Would they also sometimes make the choice to skip it? Of that he was unsure.

Dave's letter was quite clear. We would not fire someone for a simple human mistake. And, by implication, what Alisha did was a mistake, a "human error," nothing more, nothing less. Yet, for Milo watching his team, that simple description was bothering him.

Milo woke that Sunday morning to read his local morning newspaper. He only subscribed to the Sunday edition, his last attempt to hold onto a bygone era of paper news. The headline read, "Teen Driver Mistakenly Runs Red Light: Bicyclist Killed." He read on. The teen had texted "LOL" in response to a friend's message just minutes ahead of the accident. The newspaper drew the conclusion that the driver was likely texting at the time she ran the red light. It did not sit well with Milo. "Why would the headline use the word *mistakenly*?" Milo thought to himself. The teen may have mistakenly run the red light, but it didn't seem right to ignore the fact that the teen was texting when it happened – and it didn't make sense to Milo that you could *mistakenly* text. Texting required a choice and an action. Didn't everybody know, or shouldn't everybody know by now, that texting while driving would surely increase the odds that the texting driver would not see a red light ahead of her? "I'm missing something, here," Milo thought. "But I know who to call."

Later that Sunday after church, Milo reached out to his old friend, Ralph Jenkins, who was now a young psychology professor at Princeton. Ralph met with Milo that afternoon. Milo told Ralph about Alisha's event, about Dave's letter in response and about the headline in the morning paper.

"I'm struggling with the newspaper saying that teenager mistakenly ran the red light when the teen was apparently texting at the time. It just doesn't seem right to call running the red light under those circumstances a mistake. Running the red light might have been a mistake but choosing to text while driving is a choice, not a mistake," Milo said to Ralph. "And for that matter, I'm not even solid on what it means to make a mistake. My gut tells me that there are some mistakes we make that we clearly don't intend or choose. Alisha's may be one of these. But there are other mistakes that seem to involve a choice – like that teenager deciding to send an 'LOL' message while she was driving. Or somebody stealing. I mean, by definition, it's pretty hard to see stealing as a mistake. The theft just doesn't occur unless somebody chooses to steal." Milo looked at Ralph. "Can you help add some clarity here, 'cuz my head is just spinning. Seems to be a bit too much grace given to this teenager – or to a thief – to chalk it up as a mistake."

"I can give you bit of a model,' Ralph demurred, "but then I'm going to send you to the experts. You'll have to do some reading on your own. After that, we can talk through some of this stuff, but I'm telling you, it's not easy and your head is going to be spinning for a while as you try to make sense of this." Ralph went on to describe his adaptation of a simple model for human processing created within the Air Force back in the 1960s. "Perceive, interpret, decide, act," said Ralph. "It's called the PIDA model."

"Like the group that protects animals?" asked Milo.

"No, not PETA! P...I...D...A," Ralph said smiling as he spelled out the letters. Ralph went on to explain, "Four steps in the processing model. I *perceive* a big red light hanging above the road ahead. I *interpret* that light as a stoplight. I *decide* whether to stop, or not. Then, if I have chosen to stop, I somehow get my foot to release the accelerator, and move to the brake pedal. Perceive, interpret, decide, and act. It happens quite automatically throughout the day – and quite reliably."

"Not bad, Ralph, you did learn something in graduate school," quipped Milo.

Ralph ignored the comment. "Sometimes, though, it doesn't work so well. I might misperceive the light ahead. Fog rolling in, tree hanging over the road. Eyes not what they used to be. I just might not see the red light until it's too late. Unless I'm from another planet, however, I probably cannot misinterpret a big red light hanging above an intersection ahead. I could, however, decide not to stop. Lonely road, no other cars in sight. So, I decide to blow it off. I am in a hurry, under a time constraint; red lights are such an impediment to my existential journey toward freedom. Or, I do try to stop, but my foot simply misses the brake. New driver, clutch, brake, and accelerator pedals are confusing. Sometimes my foot just doesn't do what my brain signals. The point here is that while we are – generally - extremely reliable creatures, we do have our downside. We make mistakes, and we make risky choices. I agree with you that the two are different."

Ralph had just articulated the insight Milo was looking for. Milo saw them, two truths he must accept if he were to manage well. First, his employees, like himself, were inescapably fallible creatures. Call it human error as the ancients did, or a slip, lapse or a mistake as Ralph said the academics were calling it, it didn't matter. Humans did things they never intended to do.

The second truth, the one Milo was struggling with, related to free will. Given all the choices we make on any given day, and for a variety of reasons and motivations, some of them will be bad and some good. Life is full of decisions – where two paths lie ahead, one must be chosen. Both may have clear benefits; both may have unknown hazards. Often, it's a muddled mess. Sometimes, in the face of those dilemmas, we make a bad choice.

Milo thought this might explain more of what had happened in Alisha's event. Milo did not really know if Alisha simply forgot the gluten-free safety check or whether there was some element of choice in Alisha's actions that led to Patti Foster's three-day hospitalization. Dave's letter focused only on error – real life included choices. And, if he watched drivers on the road, and the things they did as they drove (eat, smoke, change clothes, text or surf the internet, read a book, apply mascara), clearly it was more than sometimes that people made bad choices.

Ralph went on to give Milo some advice. "I've been a student of psychology for a few years now," said Ralph. "There's a bunch we don't know about what makes humans tick, but I would say that here, it seems the choices your employees make are more important than the mistakes they make. We have some control over our choices. We have less control over our mistakes."

Milo nodded thoughtfully, "That makes sense. I want to hear more!"

"I have given you my wisdom, Grasshopper; time to turn you over to the master," Ralph said to Milo. "The fields of economics and psychology are coming together. Some of the best work around decision-making, the choices we make, is being done by economists."

"Economists?" Milo repeated.

"Yes. Economists. There are two I've read that you would find especially helpful here, I think. Amos Tversky and Daniel Kahneman, Israeli-American economists who worked together studying human decision-making. You need to read them. Tversky died in the 90's. Kahneman is a professor here at Princeton and I've met him. He won the Nobel Prize in Economics for his and Tversky's work around human decision-making, specifically what appear as irrational decisions. Kahneman's last book is *Thinking, Fast and Slow*. Start with it and call me when you've had time to digest it," Ralph said, getting up from his chair. Their meeting was done. Milo was on his way.

Milo read Kahneman's book. He found it gripping, opening up a world in which he had lived, but did not have the language to describe.

Everything Kahneman said was new but felt true intuitively. Humans are illogical decision-makers, and that made sense.

For Milo, it was Kahneman's operational model of the human brain that he found most intriguing. Kahneman described two brains – a System 1 brain and a System 2 brain. System 1 is subconscious reasoning, operating automatically and quickly. It is active and eager to solve problems. It hates dilemmas – dilemmas belong to the System 2 brain. System 1 is not unhappy being wrong – it comes with the territory of making decisions on the fly. System 2 is conscious reasoning. Slow and requiring lots of effort, it processes one thing at a time. It's lazy, happy to defer to the ever-willing System 1 in areas it doesn't find worth the effort – which is much of human endeavor. System 2 is the brain we think of when we typically think of our brain. If we are proud of our smarts, it is generally our System 2 brain we are thinking of.

For Kahneman, it is System 1, though, that is the real hero of the brain story. He argues that it is System 1 that makes most of our decisions. A drive or walk home from work happens with System 1 calling most of the shots. We do it as routine. On that drive or walk home, our System 2 brain might be off thinking of what we're going to have for dinner, what we're going to do on the weekend, whom we dislike at work. Meanwhile, System 1 is arguably doing the heavy lifting in getting us home – deciding when to stop, where to turn, how fast to travel.

Milo had grown up thinking that the subconscious brain was just there, not doing much, by no means the hero of any story. That is, until he read Kahneman. There was one experiment in Kahneman's book, done by English researchers that made it clear for Milo. The researchers wondered if they could influence payment for coffee in an employee break room where payment was on the honor system. In the experiment, the researchers put a small picture above the money jar. Each week the picture alternated; one week the picture was a bouquet of flowers. Pretty benign. The next week, the flowers were replaced by a set of eyes.

Crazily, the researchers discovered that people were more likely to pay when the eyes were above the money jar. They paid for their coffee more often when the picture was of the eyes rather than of the flowers. A photo of two eyes, staring at the coffee drinkers. This is where Milo could clearly see that human beings were making decisions they did not even know they were making. There was no rational reason a photo of two eyes would change the behavior of coffee drinkers. If it was in the employees to cheat the system, to avoid paying, how could two eyes change their behavior? But they did.

Intellectually, it was an anomaly. Milo wrestled with it, asking others, after explaining the experiment, if they thought the change in behavior could rightfully be called a 'choice.' Did coffee drinkers really make different choices because the eyes were present? Did they really think to themselves, "Crud. I'm being watched. I'd better pay this time?"

The difference in money paid was not human error; it was not a mistake. Milo was convinced human mistakes were inadvertent. We don't choose the errors we make. They just happen to us. He meant to pay but forgot; he meant not to pay, but did. If this were the case, we would logically expect that the money collected in alternating weeks would be roughly the same. Yet, the researchers saw a marked increase in payments when the photo of eyes was present.

Milo was convinced; humans make "choices" they don't even know they're making. The subconscious brain, what Kahneman calls the System 1 brain, is making those choices for us based, in part, upon the visual cues around us. The conscious brain, System 2 for Kahneman, knows that the eyes are not really "watching" us, (at least not in the way a security guard or camera watches) yet our subconscious brain (System 1) sees the eyes, and makes the choice that alters the coffee drinkers' behavior.

It may be a choice, but it's a subconscious one. Our System 2 brain can focus on the discussion we're having with a colleague as we pour our coffee, while our System 1 brain takes care of the payment. "Beautiful," thought Milo. "This adds another layer to human behavior that I not only hadn't considered, but I certainly didn't have the language to describe." Contrary to feeling depressed by the layer of complexity, Milo felt enlightened.

He also found the distinction between the two systems very helpful for his thinking about Alisha and her accountability in the Patti Foster event. "With Alisha, if we had disciplined her, would we have been disciplining her for a System 1 subconscious choice, or for her System 2 conscious thinking?" he wondered. Does it even make sense to discipline an employee when the System 1 brain made the decision? Milo's head was beginning to spin again...

If we do have two brains, in essence, Milo wondered, did he now have to look at each when something went awry at Dave's Subs? It seemed to Milo that it was the System 2 brain that was the real culprit when really bad behaviors were present. It seemed totally illogical to think of punishing a System 1 choice, as System 1 was not really about volitional, conscious choices. Theft, arson, slander – these required Kahneman's System 2 to be at the helm, driving these more "evil" choices.

"Only System 2, conscious thought, ought to be considered if I'm thinking about disciplining an employee – or my daughters, for that matter," thought Milo. This was all beginning to open up a door to more fully understanding what had happened in Alisha's event. What was her System 1 brain doing in those few minutes of work from the point Patti Foster made her request for a gluten-free roll? What was Alisha's System 2 brain thinking?

Milo found himself launched on a massive thought experiment of his own. Milo was out to catch his System 1 and System 2 brains at work. Milo knew this was no easy task. If System 1 were subconscious, it would by its very definition be hard to watch. And his System 2 brain, if it was watching, was probably not thinking. That said, Milo set out to watch.

For Milo, as with most experienced drivers, driving had become a System 1 task, requiring very little conscious thought on Milo's part given his years of driving experience. On his drive to work, Milo would try to think with his System 2 brain. He thought about a basic multiplication challenge while he drove, knowing it would tax that part of his brain.

The multiplication challenge, beginning at 2, multiplying that by 2, and then multiplying that product by 2 and so on was easy at first but quickly engaged his System 2 brain. He would say it in his head, "2, 4, 8, 16, 32, 64, 128, 256, 512, 1024, 2048, 4096." By the time he reached 4096, his System 2 brain was deep in mathematical computations. He would push on. He'd tax his System 2 problem solving brain, while he continued to drive to work trying to see how much of his drive was done without much control from the thinking side of his brain.

Milo's experiment stimulated both of his brain's operating systems. Milo thought it was a reasonable simulation of his store, of what his artisans faced every day. The job of artisan was to connect with the customer, to hear what they wanted, to react to their requests. And while all that was going on, the artisan's hands were fast at work, already making the customer's requested sandwich. It was as if the artisan was on autopilot making the sandwich. For a fast paced artisan, there was much in play. The System 2 brain communicated with the client, responded to queries, watched the line building, and yes, sometimes drifted off to think about something other than work. All the while, the artisan's hands continued to make sandwiches, the hands seemingly having a mind of their own.

Milo was beginning to build for himself a good model. He didn't know if Daniel Kahneman would approve of his interpretation, but it was working for Milo Alvarez. He even took a shot at simulating a college professor, at home over dinner, talking to his six-year old twins. "Sara and Emily, you might not know it, but you each have two brains," he told them.

Sara asked, "Daddy, is that because we're twins?"

"No," he laughed. "When most of us think of the word 'choice' we think of a slow, deliberate process; a very smart man called this part of our brain 'System 2.' Choosing a college, choosing a mate, choosing which Barbie doll you're going to donate to the homeless shelter are generally slow, deliberate tasks.

"Choosing between chocolate and vanilla ice cream at Johnny's birthday party, while he's opening up all his presents? Well, that's probably going to be less than deliberate. Your System 2 brain is going to be most focused on the presents because they're really cool and you're wishing that you were the one having the birthday. Nonetheless, your System 1 brain will choose, because you don't want to miss out on your favorite desert. Your mouth will tell Johnny's mom, 'I want vanilla, thank you.' But here's the thing, did you really make a choice? Yeah, to some degree you did. Did you weigh the pros and cons of vanilla vs. chocolate ice cream, however? No. Did you recall all of your earlier experiences, asking yourself which was more satisfying, chocolate or vanilla? No. Yet, in the blink of an eye your System 1 brain made a choice."

Sara and Emily stared at their dad. Said Emily, speaking for both herself and Sara as she was prone to do, "Daddy, we don't know what you're talking about, but can we have some ice cream after we finish our green beans?"

While his daughters did not seem to appreciate the brilliance of Kahneman's thinking, Milo was beginning to believe that understanding the differences between System 1 and System 2 thinking was critical. To produce good outcomes at Dave's Subs, Milo had to help his artisans make good choices. And, as Kahneman pointed out, those choices came from two different places.

It was clear to Milo that he was going to have to look at the design of the systems in which he was requiring his sub artisans to work. Even in a perfectly designed system, Milo knew errors would still happen – they had to given the fallibility of not only the humans who designed the systems (he and Dave), but also of those who would work within the system they had so carefully and fallibly designed. Still, Milo thought, the better the system design, the better the choices of his employees, the better the outcomes he should get. Accountability, for Milo, was coming into focus – it was mostly about the quality of his artisans' choices, at the conscious and subconscious level.

It was one thing for Milo to see a hazard and choose, with his System 2 conscious brain, to ignore it. It was another to be on autopilot, thinking of something with his System 2 brain, while his System 1 brain made a risky decision. Milo was convinced that Kahneman's System 2 brain should be held accountable differently than should the System 1 brain. While the System 2 brain had to make conscious, volitional choices, the System 1 subconscious brain was off making decisions that System 2 didn't even know were being made.

Milo thought of that quintessential question asked by the police officer, "Sir, did you know you were doing 10 mph over the speed limit?" Milo was convinced he could now ask the officer a legitimate question in return. "Officer, are you speaking of my System 1 brain or my System 2 brain? Because, frankly, my System 2 brain was thinking about what kind of career Elvis would have had if he'd lived longer, and well, my System 1 brain, I have no idea what it was aware of. So, officer, the answer is, uh, it depends."

This distinction between System 1 and System 2 brains had very practical implications for Milo's workplace, and for the Patti Foster event specifically. Was Alisha's failure to check that the roll was gluten-free a conscious choice? Did her System 2 thinking brain contemplate the risks of not checking? Or did her System 1 brain simply choose for her? Did her System 1 brain shed some mental and physical load, given the stresses of being manager and sub artisan at the same time? Or did she recognize the risks of not looking, but chose to skip a critical customer safety check because, unbeknownst to Milo, she despised Patti Foster and somehow had an uncanny ability to recognize that Patti Foster suffered from celiac disease?

Milo didn't think that was likely, but he did believe he was gaining a deeper understanding of his employees. And, for that matter, his wife, his children, and himself.

YELP

The downturn at Store #6 hit Charles and Bryce the hardest. Of course Alisha took it hard; that goes without saying. But Charles and Bryce seemed to own Alisha's mistake. They didn't make the mistake personally, but they took ownership as if the team had made the mistake. For Milo, it was an interesting perspective.

A few weeks after Alisha's return, after the store had closed for the day, Charles and Bryce approached Milo with an idea.

"Milo, you got a minute?" asked Charles.

"Yeah, I do," said Milo.

"We've been feeling terrible about the loss of business since that Patti Foster thing. And we have an idea to help out," said Bryce.

"What's your idea?" asked Milo.

"You know that I'm a programmer," said Charles. "We talked about it in my interview and about how I've made web pages for the family and all the grand kids and help them get set up on social media - with their parents' permission, of course. You may not know this, but Bryce is an amateur photographer."

"Yeah. We'd like to set up a website for Dave's Subs, with the different locations and rework the Yelp listing with links back to our website," said Bryce. "I know it makes a difference if there's a website link from the Yelp page. It allows people to see our menu. I can take photos of some of our different sandwiches. And we could even have a page with team members and their photos and their bios – kinda make it more personal for our customers. Or make avatars for us." Bryce was getting animated as he thought out loud of potential ideas.

"Bryce and I can work content together. Bryce will do the photos and I'll do the programming," Charles added. "We can get a beta page set up and you and Dave can approve it. I'll even get the grandkids to go on and try to break it so we know all the links are working. Our menu isn't complicated or all that varied. I think we could have this up and running in two or three weeks, easy."

"You guys, that's very nice to offer. But I'm not sure Dave's in a position to fund that," said Milo. "You know, the Patti Foster lawsuit sorta emptied the bank account, from what I can tell."

"We're not here asking for additional paid work," said Bryce, a little offended. "We're here offering our time to help our business. We'll even redesign the comment cards to add a 'How'd you hear about us?' line so Dave can track whether the website makes a difference. If it doesn't, he pulls it. If it does? Well, he goes from there.

"And besides," added Charles, "this gives us a chance to flex our creative muscles – keeps me up to date with the grandkids and gives Bryce a chance to take some photos - which he does all the time anyway. Heck, down the road, we can use the website to offer free subs on Patti Foster day!"

Milo cringed. "I don't think I'll take that part of the plan to Dave, but I will take the rest of it." Dave looked at his two sub artisans. "I really appreciate your teamwork and initiative. This hasn't been easy on any of us."

Dave wisely and gratefully accepted Charles and Bryce's offer to build a website and manage the Yelp listing. The website went live in less than two weeks. The website was clean with just the right infusion of hip. And the photos Bryce took were stunning. Dave mentioned to Milo that as soon as the store had recovered the lost revenue from the Patti Foster mishap, he was going to commission Bryce to create photos for all the Dave's Subs stores.

It was, for Milo, a very visible example of going above and beyond the call of duty. Charles and Bryce's website work was obviously not part of their job description as artisans. It was Charles and Bryce voluntarily taking the initiative to do more than was required. It was a refreshing opportunity for Milo to take his thoughts off Alisha and human error, and turn to something much more positive.

This was different. This behavior, this decision, was totally in the control of Charles and Bryce. Why would they choose to give the extra effort? Why would they do more than was required? Sure, at the end of the day, making subs was what mattered. Without getting those subs out the door, there would be no need for a website. How many subs could an employee produce? That was the core measure. But beyond that core measure there were intangibles, such as Charles and Bryce's extra effort off hours to help build a website and to facilitate a good presence on Yelp. Milo wanted to remember their effort when it came time for reviews. It wasn't the core measure, but it must certainly count for something.

Milo's focus shifted from bad, or undesirable events, to the work of his team as a whole. What did each team member bring to Dave's Subs? How should he evaluate their contribution as a whole? Milo knew he would need to answer these questions as he worked out his system of workplace accountability.

PABLO'S

Dave has always been a car buff, dreaming of owning a nice sports car, a British Aston Martin, or Italian Maserati. Not too sporty like a Ferrari or Lamborghini, something just a little more civilized and stately, but still fast.

Dave also enjoys racecars and racing. Racing that showcases the kinds of cars he likes. So, for Dave, it's Le Mans racing. The big manufacturers bring prototype cars with 1000 horsepower to the track, and then they bring their more tame 600 HP versions that look a bit more like everyday cars, like the Aston Martin that Dave so coveted. All the cars race together on the track. Le Mans racing is timed for distance. The team who drives the farthest over the time period wins the race. Each class of car, from the prototypes to the GT2 and GT3 production classes has a winner.

The ultimate Le Mans race, 24 Hours of Le Mans takes place every year in Le Mans, France, the first or second weekend of June. For Dave, going to the Le Mans race in France was a bucket list dream for the distant future. At the best of times, flying to Europe for a car race, even if it was the world's ultimate race of speed and endurance for both car and driver, was an extravagance that a father with two young sons, a mortgage, and a small business simply could not justify. And in the few months post Patti Foster event, it was far from the best of times.

That is, until his friend Erik sent him the text. Erik was an old college buddy who left New Jersey after graduation for a high paying oil refinery job in Texas. Erik shared his interest in cars – and his fantasy of attending Le Mans.

"Dude, it's here. It's in Austin. They've built a track, 16 turns and 3.2 miles of the most beautiful auto racing in the United States!" texted Erik. Dave felt Erik's excitement through the text message. Le Mans was coming to the United States, modified to six hours instead of the 24, but the best Le Mans cars were coming, and they were coming to Texas. With the full support of his wife, who was worried about the strain Dave was under from the Patti Foster event, Dave booked a flight from Newark to Austin.

It was a lovely Saturday. Dave and Erik showed up with three teenagers in tow, Erik's nephew and two of the nephew's buddies who loved cars and racing. Had it been a NASCAR race, the stands would have been breaking capacity, but this was a new track, and Le Mans racing was new to America. Still, Dave and Erik and their teenage entourage were five of tens of thousands of people who showed up at the track for this inaugural Le Mans race in the US.

Racing took much of the day, and it went well if well meant a lot of deep, loud engine rumbling as cars barreled between the turns, accelerating, braking, accelerating, and braking. Dave's pick for the winners in each class were all wrong, but the racing was still fantastic.

For Dave and Erik, total joy - short of one very minor event.

Dave's plane had hardly touched down in Newark before he was on the phone to Milo. Milo and Dave had spent a lot of time together in the immediate aftermath of Alisha's mistake, hashing out a way forward. In that short time, and throughout Milo's tenure at Dave's Subs, Dave had recognized in Milo a kindred spirit, someone who tended to see the world and its events slightly askew from the mainstream, and whose somewhat slanted view took him in unusual directions as he tried to figure out the world. What had happened in Austin at the race bordered on surreal, a Salvador Dali-ist experience that Dave needed to share with Milo.

"So how were the races?" Milo asked Dave, somewhat surprised to be hearing from him so soon after his return.

"Wonderful, awesome!" said Dave. "I've never been to anything like it."

"Cool. I wish I'd been there," said Milo.

"I wish you had, too," said Dave. "Not for the racing, but to experience Pablo's."

"Pablo's?" responded Milo.

"Yeah, it's a Mexican fast food vendor out at the track," said Dave.

"So are we diversifying into Mexican food?" asked Milo.

"No. It's just that I wish you were there to really experience all that is Pablo's, the food vendor," said Dave.

"That good?" asked Milo.

"No! That terrible!" said Dave.

"I don't get it. You wish I'd been with you at the Le Mans race in Austin, Texas, so that I could have experienced rotten Mexican food with you?" said Milo.

"Not the food! The food was fine. I wanted you to experience Pablo's ordering system," said Dave.

"OK, you've got my attention. What happened?" asked Milo.

"So, Erik, my friend, brings three teenagers with him. One was his nephew, the other two the nephew's friends. Five of us total. We decide to get out of the stands for a bit, hit the head, and eat some food there at the track. Outside the brand new grandstands, actually built underneath the grandstands, was a row of fast food vendors. I don't know for sure whether they were owned by the track proprietors or merely leased to outside restaurants. The names of the shops weren't national chains, so I'm guessing they were local stores, or perhaps owned by the track itself. Anyway, wanting Mexican food, we chose Pablo's."

"So what made it so terrible?" interjected Milo.

"It was their system for processing orders," said Dave. "And boy did it make me believe we got it right with single artisan workstations."

"Really. Now you've got me interested," said Milo.

"So, here's how it went down. I offered to pay, as those teenagers came without much cash and I wanted to treat my college buddy. I ordered first. The attendant running the register was a nice enough guy. There were probably 10 cash registers stacked along the 50-foot wide counter. About half of them were in operation. I placed my order. Extreme nachos and a very large diet cola. Erik ordered next. Forget what he got. Then the three teenagers lined up and ordered. I was first in line, and I was paying. But as the teenagers ordered, I just backed away waiting for Erik to finish ordering so we could catch up on family news." Dave paused. "That's another thing. It was so loud at the track. Even shouting at the top of our voices, we had a hard time holding a conversation while we were in the stands. Anyway, as the last teenager ordered, I pushed my way back up to the counter to pay. I don't know, it was something like $80 or $85 bucks."

"85 *dollars*?" said Milo.

"Yeah, it was really expensive at the track – like airport food. Captive audience," said Milo. "Anyway, back to the story. And here's where it gets good. I paid the attendant, he gave me a receipt, and then he asked me the strangest thing. A request. 'Could you please tell me again what you ordered?' he asked."

"Didn't he just take your order?" said Milo.

"Oh, yeah, he sure did," the volume on Dave's voice was rising. "He told me that he did not remember, given that there were five of us in the group. I mean, really. I told him *I* had no idea what we ordered – given that there were five of us in our group, and *I* wasn't paying attention to what other group members had ordered. How would I know what those teenagers ordered? Really, was it my job to pay attention to their order? So, I asked him, sarcastically, I'm sure, why he needed to ask me given that it was right there in his computer cash register. You guessing where this is going, yet?"

"No idea," responded Milo still waiting for the juicy part of the story.

"He told me that he needed to write it down so that a runner would then run the order back to the kitchen. And, he explained, the receipt that printed out did not show what was ordered. Only the total," said Dave.

"No way. You're kidding? No way." Milo was sputtering. "You're telling me that the guy punched the orders into a computer, and *then* had to write down the orders for a runner to take the order back to the kitchen?" asked Milo. "Did he use one of those old school green waitress pads with the tear off sheet to hang on clothespins back in the kitchen?"

"Yeah, probably," said Dave. "It was wild. There were probably five or six groups of people just hanging in front of the counter for what seemed like days to get their food. I was dumbfounded. And I couldn't take it. We had to ask three or four times for our food. A runner would bring out things one at a time, raise it up in the air and ask 'who ordered the chicken tacos?' I finally asked to talk to the manager," said Dave.

"What did she say?" said Milo.

"She said that was their system. A person takes the order, then writes it down for a runner to take back to the kitchen. The cash register is not connected to the kitchen. I mean, this is a brand new racetrack, state-of-the-art facility, and the cash register cannot cue the kitchen on what has been ordered? It's crazy."

"It's dumb," said Milo.

"I was mad. Those tickets to the race were not cheap, and I wanted to see the race, not wait in line for 20 minutes because they had a jacked up system. I did get a little mouthy with the manager. She offered no resolution. She seemed befuddled. She seemed as befuddled by me as I was by her totally jacked up system," said Dave.

Milo laughed.

"I was really probing when I was talking to the manager. Yeah, I wanted my food, but I also wanted to know how they came up with that design. My questions just frustrated the manager. It was like she could not understand why I thought the system was so screwball, as if she'd never seen modern restaurant ordering registers. Finally the manager just said to me, 'what would you have us do?' I told her I would shut down until she found a better system," said Dave.

"How'd that go over?" asked Milo.

"Not very well. But it was satisfying for me," said Dave. "Anyway, it made me think about our system and what it's like for our employees working in it. I mean, I have never seen a worse fast food design than this. Between the kitchen and us were five people on cash registers and another five or six runners. All looking helpless. It virtually guaranteed a slow, miserable experience - for everybody, customers and employees. I wasn't the only one who was frustrated. I was just one of the more polite ones." said Dave.

"So what's the moral of the story?" asked Milo. "Why are you telling me the story?"

"Well, because it hit me that good human beings have to work awfully hard to overcome bad system design. After I had my nachos, my full stomach tempered my attitude. I was getting really upset with those 10 or 11 people manning the Pablo's counter. But they were helpless. Whoever designed that system, though, *they* should be shot!" said Dave.

"Would you apply the same criteria to the man who cooked up the idea to purchase the Wally's Weiner truck?" asked Milo, chuckling.

"Heeey, watch it," said Dave. "That truck's been good for us!"

It was a good conversation for Milo. Entertaining. But more importantly than that, it was a chance to think about system design. Employers create the systems in which employees work. Milo could see that at the micro level, individuals often designed their own workspace. How an artisan sets up their workstation, how an office employee plans their day – the individual employee often decides these things. But some things, often the bigger things, are set up by the organization.

The employees at Pablo's were stuck in a terrible system. Holding them accountable for customer satisfaction when they were working in a system designed to create dissatisfied customers was difficult, if not impossible – and certainly unfair to the employees stuck in it. For Milo, the clear lesson of Dave's weekend in Austin was that Pablo's was responsible for the system they designed around their employees – and by extension for the satisfaction or dissatisfaction of its customers. Even the best employees were going to have trouble overcoming a terrible system.

WILD BILL

Dave had chosen not take his attorney's advise. He did not fire Alisha. That led his attorney to make a second recommendation: hire a consultant to make sure that the system they have in place around gluten-free rolls is well designed.

Dave's outside counsel had a point. While Dave saw justice in not firing Alisha, the general public might not. And if Alisha did make that same mistake again, give a regular roll loaded with gluten to a customer suffering from celiac disease? Well, there would be one very big "we told you so" coming Dave's way. Legally, it would open up Dave for what his attorney called "negligent retention" - retaining an employee who should have been fired.

Dave decided to take his attorney's advice and hire a consultant his attorney recommended. His name was Bill Brothers. Dave's attorney called him "Wild Bill" for his resemblance in looks and mannerisms to Wild Bill Hickok.

Currently living in Scranton, Pennsylvania, this Wild Bill was expensive; Dave and Milo would have just a half-day at Milo's store with their consultant.

"Howdy, partner," said Dave as Wild Bill came through the front door of the store. Dave didn't much like consultants, and his irreverence was obvious.

"Well, that's a greeting I rarely get. Apparently my reputation precedes me," said Wild Bill.

"Yeah, Winston, my attorney who recommended you, has shared some stories," said Dave. "At any rate, we're pleased to have you here at Dave's Subs. I'm Dave Adams and this is Milo Alvarez, my manager at this store." Dave looked around at the store, "This is where it happened."

"Well, it's a pleasure to be here. My old Aunt Martha still lives up the road in Newark, so I just couldn't turn down 'ol Winston when he asked me to help," said Wild Bill.

"So do you go by Wild Bill?" asked Milo.

"Oh, no, that's just a reputation I garnered in my youth. No reason to keep it up. Bill will be just fine," said Bill. "So, let's dispense with the pleasantries. Take me to the scene of the crime, boys."

Milo proceeded to walk Bill through the process they had in place, from delivery of the bread to serving at an artisan's workstation.

"That's a bugger you had to give that gluten-filled roll to a lawyer. Couldn't it have been a social worker, or schoolteacher, or some other less-likely-to-sue artsy-fartsy type?" said Bill.

Neither Dave nor Milo responded to that comment, uncertain whether Wild Bill was being serious or not.

"OK, I'm getting the idea. Pretty robust, it appears," said Bill. "So do you watch your team go through each of these steps?"

"Of course," said Milo.

"And do they always comply?" asked Bill, dragging out that last word as if to give Milo some time to really think about it.

"I'm thinking you already know the answer to that," responded Milo.

Dave was stepping back at this point, as if to watch a duel brewing.

"Milo? It is Milo, isn't it?" asked Bill, firing the first shot.

"Yes," responded Milo.

"You're pretty smart to think I can guess your sub makers are occasionally skipping a few of these steps. Human beings, they're pretty predictable," said Bill. "I'm guessing you pretty much always check that the bread is properly stocked. And I'm guessing your sub makers are generally going to the right location to grab their roll. But that hold up the sub in the air thing, that's gonna take a hit when the pace picks up. You've gotta have a great culture to keep that one going."

"Yeah, our artisans, that's what we call sub makers, will occasionally miss it. I'll talk to them if I see them deviate from the procedure," said Milo.

"And how's that working for you?" asked Bill.

"Pretty good, I'd say my artisans are at 95% compliance with that verbal check," said Milo.

"That's good, that's good," Bill said cheerfully, looking right at Milo.

"OK. Let me take you through some concepts, if you don't mind," said Bill.

"Sure, we're in. Always up for learning," said Dave.

"I want to teach you four concepts. I want to teach you about performance shaping factors, about barriers, about redundancy, and about recovery. It's about system design, about you designing a system that will ensure that giving a gluten roll to a lawyer doesn't happen again," said Bill.

"Let's talk about barriers first. These are the things we put in place to prevent specific human errors. Like each key in your pocket is a barrier, keeping you from wandering home to the wrong house, so to speak. One door, only one key that fits. Keeps the criminals from invading your kingdom. Matter of fact, I saw a barrier pulling into your parking garage out in the back of this building. That big 'ol pipe hanging about 7 feet above the entrance, and that big 'ol sign letting us know we're gonna hit something if our trucks' too tall. Have to be pretty low for my Porsche to not fit," he laughed. "So we got any barriers here in your store?"

Dave and Milo thought for a few seconds. Nothing was coming to mind.

"Nope, I don't think you do. The only barrier you could consider is not serving gluten-free bread in the first place. It's an option, but I'm guessing one you're not gonna choose," Bill said looking right at Dave.

"That's alright," said Bill. Folks with celiacs gotta eat, too! Now - redundancy. It's the idea of having multiple channels to the good outcome available. If one fails, you got another channel that'll get you there. You got redundancy in having multiple artisans. You got multiple food vendors should one have some unexpected catastrophe?" asked Bill.

"Yeah, we do. Sometimes we have to call a second vendor if we're not happy with the quality of the first. We try to use locally sourced ingredients, so redundancy is very important to us," said Dave, feeling proud of his system of food suppliers.

"OK, good. Now redundancy helps when we're talking availability, but our problem here is too much availability. I mean, too much availability of gluten-filled subs. So, I'd say redundancy is not gonna help us here."

"What about the second artisan checking the roll?" asked Milo, not really following that last bit of wisdom from Bill.

"Good point, Milo. Six of one, half dozen of the other, I guess. What I mean is that's probably more in the bucket of recovery. Recovery is the task we add to catch an upstream error. That check, performed both by the first and second artisan is really there to catch the mistake of the first artisan grabbing the wrong roll. Sorta redundant checks, when that roll is held up in the air. Two channels, if you may. Both, though, trying to catch that mis-grab by the first artisan," said Bill.

"Or to catch the mis-stock by the delivery man?" asked Dave.

"That's right, Dave. Good catch. And what you just did was recovery, catching my error," said Bill.

"And what is it that led you to be a consultant in this area?" asked Milo.

"Oh, I don't know. I have no background in the restaurant industry. Actually, I'm an old human factors investigator for the National Transportation Safety Board. Organizational psychologist by training, systems designer and evaluator by practice. Humans are humans, no matter where they work. I just try to help piece them together in a functional way," said Bill.

"Got it," said Milo.

"So, back to recovery. That's code language for the downstream opportunity to check that might catch the upstream error. We got them here. Milo, that's you checking to see that the bread was properly stocked. That's your artisan checking when she calls out the 'I've got gluten-free.' And that's the second artisan seeing that familiar crosshatch on the roll. Pretty deep, good depth for your defense. That means, we got lotsa back up," said Bill.

"So, does that mean we have a good process?" asked Dave.

"Hold on there, cowboy," answered Bill. "Let's talk about the last of my four factors first, that being performance shaping factors. That's fancy language for the system, you know, the environment in which your artisans work. What about your system or procedure increases or decreases the likelihood of a mistake?"

"And where you do you see some of that stuff here?" asked Dave.

"Well, the first obvious one is the cross-hatch on the top of the bread. Good for spotting the gluten-free. Now, on the bad side, you probably have a fast paced environment. Speed is important, I presume. The need for speed almost always works against us, except in racing. It tends to cause folks, in this case, your sub artisan, to shed some load. You know, skip a check here, skip a check there to keep up with your production demands – or just with restless customers. Those pressures aren't gonna go away, I'm guessing?"

"I hope not! Our lunch rushes are very fast paced. I'm only open 25 hours a week and if Dave's Subs is going to survive, we need lots of customers and those customers are mostly crammed into a 90 minute window," said Dave. "So, you're right, that's not likely to change. But we do make it clear to our team that safety comes first. Fast and friendly service, but not at the expense of safety," said Dave.

"Right," said Bill, as if he'd heard that line before. "OK, I think you have a pretty good process here. I'd probably only suggest one thing. Let your customers, those wanting gluten-free, in on the game. Let them participate."

"What do you mean?" asked Milo.

"Yeah, give us an example," said Dave.

"You know those little paper things you sit a beer mug on, you know to keep it from dripping on the table," said Bill.

"I think they're called a coaster," said Milo.

"Or a beermat, not that I would know," said Dave.

"Yeah, I'm more a wine and cheese kind of guy myself…but what if you had a stack of those right there on the edge of the artisan's counter. A person orders gluten-free, and the artisan immediately hands the customer a coaster, you know, before it leaves the artisan's mind. On that coaster you have a photo of the crosshatch bread and a little caption that says something about that being what the customer's roll is gonna look like. It allows the customer to participate, and it's one last visual cue for your hard-working artisan," said Bill.

"That's not a bad idea," said Dave.

"Of course it's a great idea," said Bill. "The only other thing I would add is that your managers, and that means you, Milo," Bill looked at him, "have to keep an eye on this 'I've got gluten-free' check. It's ripe for drift. The busier your artisans get, the more likely they're gonna drift," he finished.

"Wow, thank you, Bill. " Dave was genuinely grateful. "Your coaster suggestion is a great idea. And we'll continue to monitor for drift around the verbal safety check. That check has always been important to me."

"With all due respect, safety steps are always important after you cause harm like you did to that big city lawyer," said Bill. "The test will come a couple years from now, when the memory of that event has faded. That's when you'll have to reach down deep, and keep focusing on a check that appears with each passing day to have increasingly little value. Safety requires constant vigilance, my friend. It requires that you create a strong, accountable culture among your team."

Dave was surprised. It had actually been a good experience. Milo wasn't sure what to make of it.

"Well, at least he didn't compare us to Pablo's," said Dave.

"Yeah, I think we got a pretty good review," said Dave.

Within a few weeks of Wild Bill's visit, Milo and Dave had implemented Bill's suggestion of the gluten-free coaster. They were pleasantly surprised to discover that the coaster actually served a marketing purpose as well. On one side it had the big Dave's Subs logo, and on the other side it had a photo of the crosshatch roll. It said, "We serve gluten-free rolls. Look for the familiar crosshatch pattern." Milo and Dave found that customers who didn't even want gluten-free rolls took the coasters, finding them good looking enough to take with them, kind of like logoed matches at a club.

All in all, it was a good experience with Wild Bill. For Milo, it was an education on this new science of human factors. Ideas like barriers, recovery, and redundancy were new to Milo. He'd known, or worked with the concepts; he just didn't have any formal language to describe them. And performance shaping factors? That was just the system that Milo tried to build around his artisans, and tried to build around the students who came to his music studio. Milo got what Bill was saying. And it excited him, in part, because it showed him that there was some science to this stuff. Milo felt like he'd been flailing around since the Patti Foster event. Now, he had Kahneman, and he had Wild Bill. He was excited to know there were answers out there. Milo just had to find them.

NICE TRY

350 subs a day, 2000 a week, 100,000 a year. There should be no doubt that in that time, and with that volume, Milo would receive a few complaints. Lots of accolades for a job well done, a wonderful sub. Yet, a few complaints – didn't like this, didn't like that. In the past week, Milo's store was the target of two complaints, one involving Bryce, the other, Fred.

"Excuse me. Are you the manager?" began the first complaint.

"Why yes I am," Milo replied in an upbeat voice.

"Your sub maker was not nice to my mother," said the man in his early 30s. "She is new to the U.S. and speaks very broken English. It took her a minute or two to order. Your employee was pushing her to get on with the order. He was so impatient. He actually asked her if she could go to the back of the line until she decided! She finally just gave up and stepped away from his station. He was rude and pushy."

Milo apologized, even before talking to Bryce. And he offered to make a sub for the man and his mother, free of charge. Milo could see the sincerity of this man's offense at his and his mother's experience with Dave's Subs. Milo had no reason to doubt the veracity of the man's claim. He wasn't throwing Bryce under the bus, but his first priority was making it right for an upset customer. Then he could speak with Bryce.

After the rush, when the store had slowed, Milo did speak with Bryce. Bryce was quick to apologize to Milo. He knew he had upset the woman; he'd watched her walk away from his workstation. And, of course, her son saying, "That was really rude. She's just learning English. You should have given her a moment" was a good sign to Bryce that things had not gone well.

Bryce came clean with Milo about the interaction with the woman. "I sometimes lose patience with people who don't speak English," said Bryce. "It's the speed of the rush. I have subs to make, we have lines, and she's struggling to read the menu."

"OK," said Milo. "So how did you cope with that stress?"

"I told her that if she needed more time to think about her order, perhaps she could move to the back of the line," said Bryce.

"Oh, my gosh," Milo thought to himself. "Bryce," said Milo looking at him, "we can't be pushing people to the back of the line. Sure, the guy waiting for a friend's order to come through as a text message should probably go to the back of the line - we can't wait for those. But this was an elderly lady who was having trouble reading and speaking English."

"Milo, I know," responded Bryce. "I get fidgety. I get anxious during the rush. Maybe this isn't the best job for me."

"I'm not saying that," said Milo. "You're a good artisan. I just need you to keep your cool. Call me over if you have one of those customers. I'll help with the order while you tend to the next person in line."

While not a psychologist, Milo could see that Bryce carried some baggage from his life as a refugee and orphan. It was easy for Bryce to become anxious. Milo also knew, though, that the reality was we all have quirks, disabilities as it were. Bryce, for whatever reason, was an anxious person. Milo, as his manager could work around it. If Bryce got stressed, Milo could help.

The second event happened the same day. It involved a receipt. Dave's Subs was high tech. It didn't take cash – debit or credit card only. And unlike some stores, it didn't email receipts. That was too slow. Anything that slowed the process was systematically removed. It was all about getting 240 subs sold during the lunch rush. So, it was paper receipts.

Fred was a jokester, always engaging his customers. If there was a laugh to be heard during the rush, it was more often than not coming from Fred's workstation. Milo was convinced that his joking around could be a significant factor in his less that desired subs-per-rush stats. Milo also knew it was in Fred's nature to push boundaries. On this day a boundary got crossed.

A woman, in her early twenties Milo guessed, approached Milo with a receipt in her hand. She was strikingly beautiful, wearing a bright yellow sundress. "Are you the manager?" she asked.

"Yes," Milo replied, clearing his throat.

She then held up a receipt for Milo to see. It had one word written on it in deep red indelible ink: "Wow!"

"Your employee's being a little too friendly," said the young woman.

Milo's mouth twisted and turned, thinking, but not saying what Fred had written on the receipt. "I am so sorry, Miss. I'll talk to him."

"I'm flattered," she said, "but it did cross the line."

"Again, please accept my apologies," said Milo as he took the receipt from her.

Milo was quick to act on this one. He headed right to Fred's station, where Fred was piling meat on a sub roll for his next customer, and put the receipt in front of Fred's face, so that Fred could see it, but away from the view of his customer. "Are you kidding me?" Milo said, shaking his head as he walked away. Milo didn't want a dialogue with Fred. He only wanted to put Fred on notice that his conduct was not acceptable at Dave's Subs.

Two events. In one, the artisan was overly friendly. In the other, the artisan was not friendly enough. By this time, Milo thought, his employees should understand what was meant by "fast and friendly" service. Milo committed to talking to his employees about it. He would have a pre-shift meeting about being friendly. Now, he just had to define what it meant to be friendly.

That night, after dinner, Milo sat down with his iPad, opened a note and began writing. He was going to write down what it meant to be friendly. So he wrote *friendly* as the header. He thought, for a second, and wrote a second word, *nice,* under the heading. To be friendly was to be nice. "OK, that wasn't very helpful," Milo said to himself.

"Always greet the customer with a smile," he wrote.

"Welcome to Dave's Subs. What may I get you?" he further wrote.

"Thank you for visiting Dave's Subs."

Milo was getting an eerie feeling that he was creating a script. It sort of reminded him of the help desk at the company that produced his laptop computer. If he proceeded to write the script, customer interaction with his artisans would be like talking to a computer. That path was not going to get him very far. Milo knew, too, that the script describing the behavior he wanted to see would not include the behavior at hand, the behavior he didn't want to see.

Milo put his iPad down, and picked up his game controller. Time to take his mind off of this task for a while.

Twenty minutes of multi-player war games, and Milo's thinking was rejuvenated. Milo picked up his iPad and began again on the list, only this time instead of writing the script, he started more on point: the acts he did not want to see.

"Don't send them to the back of the line."

"Don't hit on the customer."

"Don't spit in their sub."

It only took three lines for Milo to realize that this path was not going to get him very far either. He could not create an all-inclusive list of "unfriendly" acts. It was not within his capacity. Human behavior was too diverse to create a list of all unfriendly acts.

It forced Milo to rethink his strategy. *Friendly* was not an act that could be specified. It was not a procedure. Yet somehow we all knew what it was. And it was something we valued. Dave's customers valued "fast and friendly" service. "Perhaps I'm overthinking this," he thought to himself. Maybe he should consider it as simply a "value" and leave it at that.

"*Friendly* is one of those 'I know it when I see it' kind of things," Milo thought. "I cannot tell you what friendly is. But I can surely see unfriendly, and I can also see overly friendly." Friendly is a value, abstract, for sure, but both complaints earlier that day made it clear that people were certainly willing to judge conduct against abstract values.

There were other values, of course. Clearly, safety was an important value. We could see unsafe acts, like a sneeze in a customer's sub, and unsafe things in our environment, like a broken, and now sharp, utensil. At the other end, we could see overly safe, like Fred coming into work wearing a hair net and mask. "Don't want to take the chance of bacterial transmission," he might say. While Milo valued safety, he'd quickly decide it just wasn't in our culture for sub shop artisans to look like they were about to perform surgery, all gowned and gloved. It's not "fast and freakishly safe" service that Dave's promoted after all.

Safe and friendly both have meaning; that's why both were articulated to every Dave's Subs employee. Likewise, unsafe and unfriendly have meaning, yet they are just as hard to define. Overly safe and overly friendly suffer the same fate – important, but hard to define. Yet, Milo knew when he saw them in context, they were as clear as the night sky. We know unsafe when we see it. We know overly friendly when we experience it. It was not something Milo could, or need, spell out in detail. Human beings had brains that could handle abstract concepts, and that was exactly what Milo could expect from his artisans, that each one of them respect the two values of safe and friendly service.

Milo held the meeting the next day. A short, stand-up huddle about friendliness. "I want to talk about the "friendliness" part of fast and friendly," Milo began. "We value being friendly here at Dave's Subs. It's a core value here. Sometimes, with our best efforts, our customers might not experience what they think of as friendly. They will let us know. Just try your best. If we make a mistake, we learn. Just don't proceed when you know what you're about to do risks being seen as unfriendly, or even overly friendly," he said, looking directly at Fred as he finished his statement.

"How will we know?" asked Esther.

"We all know what it means to be friendly," said Charles. "When we get close to being unfriendly, or overly friendly, there will be that little voice telling us we're too getting close."

Milo looked at Charles as if he'd been reading his mind. "Like Charles said, that little voice in your head should be telling you when you're too close to the edge," said Milo.

Finding the Hidden App

Milo continued in his study of Kahneman's System 1 and System 2 brains. He marveled at what he could do without thinking about it. He could ride a bicycle without having to tell his legs to lift, push, lift, push. And that part about controlling the handlebars? It seemed to happen automatically. Most of what his body did seemed directed by a part of his brain that was not the part where he did his thinking.

Milo decided one morning to ride his bicycle to work. It was another beautiful summer day and the car had become too easy to drive for his System 1/System 2 thought experiment. Milo wanted something more difficult to explore. So off he went, riding and thinking. Milo decided, in a twist to his experiment, to see if he could create a mental list of iconic rock-and-roll songs starting with his parents' generation and using successive letters of the alphabet. *American Pie* by Don Mclean, Springsteen's *Born to Run*, *Comfortably Numb* by Pink Floyd, and the list went on. It was a very taxing endeavor. When she found out, Milo's wife, Isabel, told him he was crazy and was going to kill himself playing his game.

"Why don't you just focus on the road?" she asked, a little snappishly.

And, of course, Milo would think, but not say, "*Nobody's* thinking about driving when they're driving." That was a marital debate not worth provoking...

So there he was, riding his bike to work, somewhere in the H/I stage of his list, just remembering *Hotel California* by the Eagles, when it happened. Two pre-teen boys up ahead were walking in the same direction as Milo was riding. They were playing with a soccer ball. In an instant, Milo saw the ball get away from them, and the boy closest to the street running out to grab it, heedless of traffic. In front of him, Milo saw the oncoming cars. Behind him, Milo heard the oncoming cars.

While working on his very complex mental activity, Milo marveled that he could engage in an even more complex physical exercise – listen with his ears, watch with his eyes, pedal with his feet, steer with his arms, balance himself on two wheels with his body and inner ear – all without thinking at all.

And then, suddenly, there were the boys. And the ball. And all those cars moving in all directions. He had effortlessly ridden his bicycle while focusing, with great effort, on his mental music catalog and the next song on his list. That is, until he saw the ball get away from the boys ahead. His eyes caught the ball moving into the street, and the boy closest to the street instinctively chasing it. In the blink of an eye, Milo's System 2 brain was on the ball and the boy. He quickly looked back to see how close the traffic was behind him, and then turned to look again at the boy reaching for the ball.

Milo's fingers hit the brakes, his feet left the pedals and planted on the street; he came to a quick and complete stop. Milo did not follow the boy into the street, but he did instinctively yell even though he was much too far away to have any impact on the outcome. He could only stand and watch, his full attention on the tragedy about to happen. Had it not been for the quick reaction of the car approaching from in front of Milo, and that driver's immediate stop, Milo might very well have witnessed a tragedy.

Milo stood still, his bike beneath him, well after the two boys were on their way. He had been too far away to actually rescue the boy, but his heart was still racing. Taking a few minutes for his anxiety to subside, Milo got back on his bike, and continued on his way to work, too wobbly to continue playing his music game.

His mind, his thinking brain, was now on another query. Clearly, something had happened, for him and for the driver of the approaching car. He suspected that the driver was where Milo was, distracted from the task of driving down the road, thinking about work, life, kids, or in Milo's case, song titles. Yet, in the blink of an eye, both he and the other driver reacted.

Milo considered his developing System 1/System 2 model. Something significant had just been revealed in that near miss with the boy, the ball and the car. Somehow, his mental process was interrupted, causing his highly engaged System 2 brain to stop its music catalog-generating task and immediately turn its attention to the ball and the kid moving into the street. It appeared to Milo that something in his brain was monitoring the world around him. Something was paying attention when his System 2 brain was otherwise engaged. Was this part of his System 1 subconscious machinery or something different?

Milo quickly came to the conclusion that something was indeed monitoring the world around him, separate from his System 1 or System 2 brain. It was like a mobile phone app. It launched when he woke up in the morning, and it quietly watched the world around him, looking specifically for hazards. "Heck, it even watches while I'm asleep," Milo thought to himself, thinking of the times he'd woken from a sound sleep because one of his daughters had fallen out of bed or a patio door left unlocked had blown open in the night.

Always running, constantly looking for risk. "It's an internal risk monitor," Milo thought to himself. "It stands guard to the world around me."

Milo thought back to the two anthropology courses he'd taken in college. Milo pictured his early ancestors, sitting around the campfire on some African savannah, three lions circling in the grass around them. A misstep by one, the sound of a broken twig. "Alert, Alert," a collective risk monitor would scream to the humans enjoying their evening fellowship.

Those who didn't have the risk monitor application installed, or lacked the latest update, became the lion's dinner – end of the bloodline. Those with the updated app installed got a few moments' notice to take action, to avoid a dreadful fate.

It was so clear now – a risk monitor, continually running in the background behind his System 1 and System 2 brain – that Milo was surprised it had taken him 34 years to put a name to it. Milo was convinced. If Kahneman's System 1 and System 2 were useful constructs, so too was Milo's own construct of an internal "risk monitor."

Tooling down the road on his bike, System 1 doing the driving, System 2 thinking about his music catalog, Milo's risk monitor was silently but constantly working in the background. The ball rolls into the street; his risk monitor fires. But which brain does it alert? Did Milo's subconscious System 1 brain automatically react? Possibly, if the hazard was large. Did his conscious System 2 brain react? Yes, again when the risk was large. In this situation with the boys, Milo's risk monitor sent the signal to his conscious brain, "Hello there! There's a boy running into the street! Time to stop thinking about song titles. Time to assess. Time to slow down!"

Like everything new for Milo, he began to play with the idea in his head. He watched others, his wife and his two daughters in particular. They were his laboratory, as were his employees, and fellow drivers on the road. He quickly realized his own shortcomings around the risk monitor. It wasn't that Milo's risk monitor was not well tuned. It was instead how he reacted to others whose risk monitor did not fire when he thought it obviously should. The disparity was causing some real problems.

It looked like this: "Honey, geez, how could you not see that...?" Milo would say as Isabel was driving the girls to school. It was like a tick, it just happened. "How could you not see that the car in front of us was so close?" Milo would ask. If questioned, Milo would admit that his wife probably did see the car she was following. After all, it's hard not to perceive 3000 lbs. of metal 30 feet in front of them. Yet, at a particular speed, Milo and Isabel's interpretation of risk differed.

As a passenger, Milo's risk monitor alerted before his wife's who likely felt more in control as the operator of the vehicle. It wasn't really a discussion of who did or did not see the car out their front window. It was about the operation of their respective risk monitors. Milo's went off when his wife's did not.

Milo started thinking about how differences in risk monitor firing were the culprit in many marital disputes – driving, financial decisions like whether to invest the maximum in an IRA or take the girls on a backpacking vacation in the Adirondacks, whether the girls jumping off the play equipment in the backyard was a good idea, whether it was safe to toss in one colored sweater with a load of whites – so many places where he and Isabel saw risk very differently.

Differently. But was one risk monitor more accurate and reliable than the other? Always? Were there things that made a risk monitor more or less reliable? Did the reliability of a single risk monitor change with circumstances?

These were some interesting questions. In the short time he'd been observing his and others' risk monitors, Milo knew that risk monitors were less than 100% accurate. Not everyone's risk monitor worked the same. Milo could see that his would alert when others' did not and vice versa, seemingly *ad infinitum*.

Milo was drawing some interesting conclusions about the variability and why his risk monitor sometimes failed him. First, there was the obvious. When Milo was tired and fatigued, his risk monitor would not work as well. Like the rest of his brain, it needed feeding, it needed rest, and it needed to be healthy. Intoxication or drugs, while not an issue for Milo, incapacitated anyone's risk monitor.

Milo next found that it could be overwhelmed. While it could go off while its owner was distracted by other things (which seemingly was its purpose in the first place), it could be impacted by too much load on the other parts of the brain, particularly when the hazard it was trying to pick up was relatively slight in magnitude. Milo found this at a dinner party with his wife, where nearly everyone at the party was new to him. So when Isabel asked on the way home, "Did you notice that awful plaid shirt Bob was wearing?" Milo responded truthfully, "No."

"Let me have Glenda send us a photo, before Bob takes that thing off," said Isabel.

Given modern technology, it took only a few seconds to get the photo. It took Milo only one, quick look, "Honey, there is no way Bob was wearing that. I would have been making lumberjack jokes all night long."

Yet, Bob *was* wearing that plaid shirt to the dinner party. For Milo, there were just too many unknowns at the dinner party. New people to meet, lots of names to remember. Milo just missed the shirt, when under normal circumstances that plaid shirt would have set his risk monitor clanging.

The most alarming limit Milo discovered to his risk monitor (and to others', he suspected), was the old adage that "familiarity breeds contempt" – well, if not contempt, then undoubtedly lower volume alerts. The more time Milo spent with a hazard, something that initially caused his risk monitor to fire, the less either of his brains paid any attention.

Milo found this in his new, well-used car he'd purchased a year earlier. It had a few quirks. A window that didn't seem to roll up all the way. A strange grinding noise coming from the rear differential. The windshield wiper that left a streak of unswiped rain on every pass. They were annoyingly noticeable when Milo first bought the car. Get in the car, put it in drive, and that differential would grind, the window would whistle. Start to rain, and a streak across the window appeared as soon as he turned on the wipers.

Initially, his risk monitor alerted him every time he sat in the car. It did not, however, send his wife or daughters' monitors into high-volume alert mode. "Do you hear that? Do you feel that? Do you see that?" he'd ask his wife and kids. They'd answer, "yes" but only after several prompts. For them, the inputs were not enough to make their risk monitors fire; they were thinking about other things on the way to school. And this made sense to him; as the driver, he would be more sensitive to the hazard, to the visual and aural inputs.

The problem for Milo was that he was no longer seeing, hearing or feeling those inputs. Milo had not gotten around to fixing the problems with his car; it was still making the daily trek to school and work, but his risk monitor was no longer alerting him to the problems he used to see. Familiarity was causing his risk monitor to shut down. Yet, when Milo drove with a friend in his car, the friend, car lover or not, would invariably say, "Milo, don't you hear that grinding noise?"

Milo could see that if the human on the savannah spent more time with the lions, particularly if it had been a while since the lions had had success in snatching an unwary human, the lions might appear less and less a hazard. It was clear for Milo, familiarity bred complacency. The more time spent with a hazard, the less apt the risk monitor was to fire, particularly when nothing terrible had yet happened or the terrible thing had happened in the distant past.

Milo realized pretty quickly that his growing awareness of his own risk monitor, and an understanding of just how it operated, would be important in his evolving notions of workplace justice. We expect our employees to avoid hazards, and one way we do that is with our own trusty risk monitor app. Rules help, but so too does the risk monitor. Milo expected Alisha to see the hazard of non-gluten-free bread in her hand. That's why the gluten-free rolls were kept separate from the other breads and why the bakery put the unique crosshatch pattern on the top. And that's why Dave's Subs artisans were trained and monitored on the policy to call out "I've got gluten-free!"

Could her eyes see the bread in her hand? To Milo, that seemed a given. Alisha did not seem to have any trouble with her eyesight; she didn't even wear contacts or glasses. But how did Alisha interpret what she saw? Perceive, interpret, decide, and act. She could clearly perceive (see) the roll in her hand, yet did she interpret it as the wrong roll? Was her risk monitor screaming, knocking at the door of her System 2 brain? "Hello, Alisha, you have the wrong bread in your hand!" If so, Milo thought to himself, his response to Alisha would be quite different. If she were the type of employee who would consciously ignore that warning, she did not belong at Dave's Subs.

Yet, that is not who Milo thought he had in Alisha. For the first time since the event Milo was at real peace with how he and Dave had responded to Alisha's mistake. She was a good employee. On that terrible day, at that moment when she grabbed the wrong bread and did not call out "I've got gluten-free!" her risk monitor, in Milo's view, did not fire. It was not knocking at the door of her System 2 brain. Knowing what Alisha faced on that day - filling in for Milo, Fred's angry customer, Alisha's line of waiting customers - Milo knew that Alisha was simply in the middle of a lunch rush with extra duties and doing the best she could to get through it.

Nothing in the story suggested that Alisha was at any time aware of the risk she was taking. And that gave Milo some peace. Yes, Alisha had not followed the protocol on which she'd been trained – she had, in fact, broken a rule. But that, Milo would leave for later.

For now, Alisha's risk monitor had not fired. That was what Milo needed to know. Milo had a new tool in his discovery of the hidden risk monitor app. And it could not come a moment too soon.

WALLY'S WIENERS

Dave had not lost confidence in his newest shop. That said, Milo and Dave both looked at the numbers for Store #6 — sales were down by almost 20 percent in the two months following the Patti Foster event. They thought of just giving it time, to let the press from Patti Foster's event fade into oblivion. For Dave, that seemed a less than proactive approach. Dave told Milo, "If you get the chance, use the van."

Two summers ago, Dave had asked Milo to help him out with a project at the original store. Dave had apparently spent a lot of time at county fairs as a kid and had it in his head that he needed a mobile kitchen. One of those trucks, painted in shop colors, with a big Dave's Subs logo on the side. You were a real shop when you could be there selling food at the county fair. Dave asked Milo to spec out a truck, perhaps even one set up by a now defunct restaurant. Surely Milo could help Dave find a good truck.

It took some time, but Milo did find what Dave was looking for, a truck equipped with a nearly full-size, modern diesel operated refrigerator, a truck in which employees could stand inside to make subs and serve their customers through windows on both sides of the truck. Originally built for Wally's Wieners, it was a beauty and could easily be repainted for use by Dave's Subs. Milo found the truck on Craig's List for $17,500, a bargain at about a third of the price of a brand new refrigerated truck.

Dave loved Milo's pick, but not the price. Dave ran the numbers of how many subs he'd have to sell to make a profit on the truck. While perhaps a great deal, the price was still too steep for Dave. Desperate to have a mobile kitchen now that the idea was in his head, Dave contacted his cousin Larry, an experienced van converter.

Larry had been doing automotive repair for 20 years. After listening to Dave's aspirations for a mobile food truck, Larry convinced Dave that he could purchase an old panel van for $5,000 and install a used electric refrigeration unit on the top, sort of like the ones you might see on a travel trailer or motor home. Total price, including Larry's time - $7,000. Less than half the price of the Wally's Wiener's truck, and in Dave's mind, less than half the time to recoup the cost. What a great deal...

What had started out as an idea for a true mobile kitchen, perhaps even with the capacity for running water, had morphed into an old Ford panel van with Dave's Subs' logo painted prominently on any available surface and a used electric refrigeration unit perched on the top of the roof. It had its issues, but for the last two years, it had done the job. Regularly in use, it just hadn't been used by Milo's store #6.

The dedication of a new regional park about ten miles from Milo's shop was the opportunity Milo had been waiting for. The mayor had contracted with three small businesses to cater lunch for the 600 people estimated to be in attendance. Dave's Subs was awarded a contract to provide 200 subs. It gave Milo the chance to "use the van" as Dave requested. One of Dave's Subs' employees from the original store drove it over to Store #6, parked it around back in the parking lot, and left the keys with Fred who, along with Bryce, had volunteered to staff the mobile unit on that early-August Saturday morning.

Milo was genuinely bummed that a noon piano recital with his two daughters kept him from participating in the catering for the park's dedication. Still, Milo came to the store that morning to help Bryce and Fred assemble the sandwiches they would serve at the park dedication. Upon filling the truck with the equipment and food required for the day, Milo gave Bryce and Fred a critical piece of instruction, "Remember, the refrigerator is electric. You have to plug it in as soon as you get to the park. The electrical cords are all there in the back."

With that final bit of instruction, Bryce and Fred headed out to the park about 9:30 am. Sunny and hot, already in the mid 80's, a rare heat wave would push the day's mercury to well over 90.

Dave's cousin, Larry, had assembled the mobile kitchen van using parts he had around the shop, as best he could. Some childhood issues still lingering between them, and seeking to impress his cousin Dave, Larry set up the van's electrical power in a unique way. He had an electrical connector, both the male plug and female socket from an old clothes dryer. It was one of those odd 240-volt socket and plug that didn't look like anything else in the world. When Larry installed the refrigeration unit on the top of the truck, he installed the electrical connector plug conveniently on the rear driver's side of the van, about a foot from the two back doors.

The refrigeration unit ran on standard 120V electricity, it just had this weird 240V plug on the side of the truck. To make it work, Larry assembled a three-foot long connector, on one end a standard 120V male plug, and on the other end the weird 240V adapter. Bottom line, to make the refrigeration work, Bryce and Fred needed 120V power, an extension cord to reach to the power source, and that one-of-a-kind three foot long electrical cord.

While electrically creative, Larry was equally organized and efficient. Understanding the critical nature of both the extension cords and his one-of-a-kind connector, Larry had bolted in a black plastic container inside the van, near the back, to house the three 50 foot long extension cords and that unique three foot long connector.

The black box, bolted to the floor of the van. That's where the cord was supposed to be. On that day, the cord was missing. Actually, as it turned out, it was Dave himself who had removed it from the van on the previous Saturday when he'd taken his customary Saturday morning trip to the local, independent hardware shop. Perennially amazed at the cable's novelty, Dave had pulled the cord from the plastic container at the back of the van and brought it with him to show the store's owner, an old friend from high school shop class. Distracted by reminiscing about the shop teacher and some classroom hijinks, he forgot the cable on the back seat of his mini-van when he returned home.

Bryce and Fred arrived at the park at 10:00 am without the connector cable, pulling in alongside two other vendors selected to cater to the 600 attendees at the park dedication that day. They had been careful to make sure that all of the required food had made it into the van. Bryce checked, and using good system redundancy, Fred double-checked. These two were surely not going to arrive to the park missing something critical to serving the 200 pre-made subs at the park dedication that Saturday.

Bryce and Fred worked quickly to set up the tent, a 10'x10' awning with a large Dave's Subs banner installed between the two back support poles. They set up two folding tables across the front from which they would deliver the subs. Bryce was going to take the lead on handing out the subs to attendees who would trade a food ticket for a sandwich. Attendees at the dedication would arrive over a three hour period, the Mayor's dedication was scheduled for 1:00 pm, with the park festivities, food and bounce houses operating from noon to 2:00 pm.

At about 10:45, Fred was ready to connect the refrigeration unit to the park's electrical power. It was then that he saw the three-foot connector was missing. Fred conferred with Bryce who searched the van himself. The connector was definitely missing. Fred and Bryce discussed calling Milo to see if he could find the connector cord, but that would mean interrupting Milo at his daughters' piano recital. Running out of time, Fred suggested that they keep the truck's engine running to power the refrigerator until they could distribute the 200 subs. Larry had conveniently set up the air conditioner to also run off of an inverter he wired to the engine's electrical generator. Larry did this so that the refrigerator would run while the van was in transit.

So Bryce and Fred decided they would run the engine to keep the air conditioner working. The engine strategy worked - for a while. It kept the van's internal refrigerated compartment cool for about 30 minutes - until the truck engine overheated. As Fred and Bryce quickly recognized, the engine itself had to be cooled, and *that* required air flowing over the engine's radiator. Which meant the van had to be moving and not idling in a park on a hot August afternoon. Sitting still with an air conditioner running, as anyone attempting to cross a mountain pass or desert deadlocked in traffic can attest to, is a surefire path to an overheated engine identifiable by the telltale steam rising from the hood of the vehicle.

At 1:00 o'clock, with nearly 150 of the 200 subs distributed, they had to turn off the engine. The steam rising from the engine compartment was having a noticeable deterrent effect on customers as evidenced by the steady stream of customers *away* from the Dave's Subs mobile unit when they noticed the steam.

Fred and Bryce slowly handed out those last 50 subs during the last hour. By the time the last sub was handed out, the inside of the refrigerated compartment had reached 70 degrees, per the thermometer Larry had mounted on the door to meet health code requirements. 70 degrees. Bryce and Fred could see it in those last few subs, the rolls were warm to the touch, and any lettuce hanging outside the confines of the bread was limp and droopy. A few of these final customers commented on the warmth of the sandwiches and the limp lettuce; some mumbled under their breath as they walked away.

Bryce and Fred faced a dilemma at the park that required making choices to solve that dilemma. The choices they made did not play out well. Nobody, not Milo, Bryce, Fred, or the guy that delivered the van to Milo's store thought to ensure that the complete compliment of electrical cables was in the van. At the park, neither Fred nor Bryce reached out to Milo for help, choosing to respect his time at his daughters' piano recital.

Their plan to run the engine seemed well intended, and it worked until the temperature outside the van rose to the point that the van's radiator could simply not keep up with the van standing still. It was a terrible design. While Larry was perhaps a good automotive technician, this particular van conversion left something to be desired. Milo had spec'd a good refrigerator truck; Dave chose the van conversion by his cousin Larry at less than half the price.

Clearly, in hindsight, Bryce and Fred should have stopped handing out subs when they passed the point of remaining fresh. They had a choice to make, and they, together, made the choice to keep pushing out warm subs until all 200 were delivered. In the moment, Bryce and Fred did what they thought seemed reasonable to do. And on Monday, back in the shop, they self-reported the mishap to Milo. All of the details were laid out for Milo to digest.

It was perfect. Milo need not create artificial mental exercises on his drives and bike rides to work. Saturday's event provided more than enough fodder for his new mental model.

Working through the Patti Foster event, and his and Dave's decision not to terminate Alisha, Milo had separated his world into three chunks. He'd identified what most of the world would call a human mistake, a human error. These are actions or decisions (sometimes unintended themselves) leading to unintended outcomes. Inadvertency was the hallmark of human error. Milo distinguished human error from the choices that we all make. He then split the choices into two categories – choices where the risk monitor fired and choices where it did not.

To Milo, the choices where the risk monitor fired, where it alerted his employee to some hazard seemed more culpable, more blameworthy. Milo thought to himself, "If the risk monitor did not alert an employee's System 2 brain to a hazard, I would have no reason to discipline her. If the risk monitor *did* alert the employee's System 2 brain, I would look at what choice the employee made in response. If I was going to discipline anybody, it would be based on how an employee responded to an alerting risk monitor."

Milo met with Bryce and Fred on Monday when they arrived at the shop. Bryce and Fred fully disclosed the events of the park dedication day, in part out of their frustration over the van not having a way to connect to any of the world's electrical sockets. "It's stupid," said Bryce.

"Yeah, I felt like I was on the cast of the *Beverly Hillbillies*. We asked other vendors around us if they had a connector. Some were willing to help, until they saw what was mounted on our truck," said Fred.

"One guy actually asked if he could take a photo of our van. And I don't think that was a compliment," said Bryce.

Milo continued to walk through the day's events with Fred and Bryce, all three staying after close on Monday afternoon to get it done. Milo was less than thrilled by Fred and Bryce's choice to keep handing out the subs. "Well, there was that guy with the narrow black tie who worked for the Mayor's office. He was intent on making sure we were delivering according to our contract. Creepy guy," said Bryce.

"We did the best we could. There at the end, I would just look at each sub and ask myself, would I eat this sub? And, every time, I said yes. A little hesitantly at the end, but still a yes," said Fred.

Milo looked at Fred briefly, silent. "Perhaps you weren't the right person to be asking that question," he said only half-jokingly.

Milo listened to the rest of their story. He apologized to Fred and Bryce for the missing cable. "That was my responsibility. I should have checked that it was all there before I sent you out to the park," Milo said. "And you're right, the van's got its issues."

Milo continued, "You should have stopped handing out subs, though. There would be a point where those sandwiches were not safe. And I think you crossed that point somewhere there toward the end."

"It's easy to see it now. With all of the people lined up, with that creepy guy with the tie, it was a little overwhelming at the time," said Bryce "I sure hope we didn't make anyone sick." He looked stricken.

"And you could have called me," said Milo. "You know I would have been available at any time."

"Yeah. We thought of that. We just didn't think there was anything you could do. We just wanted you to enjoy your girls' recital," said Fred.

With that, Milo let Bryce and Fred leave for the day. The store would live and learn. Nobody had gotten sick.

Milo sat for a while after Bryce and Fred left. He sat quietly thinking through his model, thinking about Fred and Bryce watching that thermometer rise. Did their risk monitors fire, alerting them to the hazard of overly warm food? If so, when? When the threat was in their System 2 brain, when they were "thinking" about the hazard, what did their conscious brains do to rationalize away the increasing risk? They kept handing out subs when they should have rolled up the tent and headed back to the shop. "Not the best critical decision-making," Milo thought to himself. "But how should I respond?"

JUSTIFIED

It was a busy Friday lunch. Everyone working hard to make subs. Alisha had the day off. Esther, Fred, Charles, and Bryce were at their workstations. Milo was prepping food and keeping track of the lines outside.

About 12:30, everyone in the store heard the crash. It was loud and unmistakable. The store was located in an office building, but its doors faced the street. Between the doors and the road stood about 30 feet of concrete. Part sidewalk, part patio because of the building's set back from the road. Instantly everyone inside Dave's Subs was looking out the window. Two cars had hit just about head on. And it looked like a passenger was thrown out of one. As soon as they noticed the body outside the vehicle, customers instinctively turned away, uneager to see what looked like a gruesome accident.

Milo ran to the office, grabbed his cell phone, and headed out toward the street. He dialed 911 as he ran toward the victim.

A crowd quickly gathered around the person in the street, apparently a passenger from one of cars. Not wearing her seatbelt, she was ejected through the front window. It was an old 1970s pickup truck. No airbags for either occupant. Luckily for the driver, he was strapped in.

The other car was a late model sedan. Its left front quarter panel took the majority of the damage, but the driver looked good. His airbag had deployed. He was dazed but had no visible bleeding or protruding body parts.

The girl in the street could make no such claim. It looked like one or both legs were broken, and she was bleeding heavily from her forehead. She needed aid, and fast.

As Milo was running toward the victim, a young woman was running into Milo's store. "Do you have any towels? She's bleeding bad," cried the young woman.

Esther heard her plea. "Sure, let me grab some," she said, running to the back storeroom.

"Let's go," Esther said to the lady standing anxiously at the door. "Has 911 been called?" asked Esther as they ran toward the street.

"Yes, I think a bunch of people have called," said the woman.

Esther was nearly finished with her paramedic training. She'd been taught triage. She knew how to slow the bleeding, how to stabilize the broken bones.

"I'm a medic," she said to the crowd surrounding the girl in the street. "Let me help." And that she did for the next three to four minutes until the ambulance arrived. At the welcome sound of the sirens in the distance, Esther looked into the girl's eyes. "Help is on the way," she told the girl. "Just hang in there."

Technically, Esther had abandoned her workstation. Milo had as well, but he was only prepping food. When the distraught young woman entered the store, asking for towels, Esther quickly looked for Milo. Not seeing him, as he'd already left the store, her eyes moved toward Charles, who was tending to his customer. "Go," Charles nodded to Esther, aware of her EMT training.

Esther turned to her customer, a middle aged man, in a gray pinstripe suit. "Sorry, gotta go," she said. Her customer did not know whether Esther could help. He certainly was unaware of her EMT training. He only knew there was an automobile accident outside, and he was standing at the front of a line with no artisan there to help him. A ten minute wait already, and just as he was about to be served, his artisan leaves. No "I'll be right back." Just a statement, "gotta go."

The fire department, with its attendant paramedics, arrived within 3-4 minutes of the accident. Things were moving fast. And Esther's two minutes with the young lady in the street looked like it had made a difference, a critical difference, to her survival

Gone only 5 minutes or so, Milo walked back into the store with Esther. Her hands were covered in blood, and Milo could see she was shaken. She was wiping her own arms with a towel as she headed toward the back room to wash her hands.

Milo headed toward the line at her workstation. Standing there alone was the man with the gray pinstripe suit, a half made sub sitting there on the counter in front of him. Milo approached. "I am so sorry," Milo said. "She needed help," he said indicating the woman still lying in the street, now surrounded by paramedics and firemen.

"That doesn't help me with my sub," said the obviously irritated man.

"But surely helping was the right thing to do?" asked Milo, somewhat incredulous.

"For who?" asked the man.

"For all of us," Milo replied. "Let me make you a new sandwich. It's on the house."

For Milo, whatever Esther did, it was justified. Regardless of what Dave's Subs owed the customer in the gray pinstripe suit, regardless of his anger, what Esther did was justified. It was easy for Milo to see, although clearly more complicated for his obviously irritated customer. As he finished the man's sub, the voice in Milo's head repeated, "The guy's a jerk! The guy's a jerk. The guy's a jerk."

Justified. That's the word Milo was using. Milo added it to his model. Rules could be broken. Expectations could be breached. If it were justified.

Who decided what was justified? That was for those who would stand in judgment. Here it would be Milo, as Esther's manager. And, in his mind, Esther had done the noble thing in providing help – particularly given her training.

HORIZONTAL BOARDING

Bryce had been telling Fred for some time that he should learn to ride a skateboard. "Time to rip. Time to shred," Bryce would say. After repeatedly telling Fred how much fun skateboarding is, Bryce one day brought his skateboard to work. Just after closing, Bryce again encouraged Fred to give it a try. "It's got four wheels, just like your car," said Bryce.

"I prefer my car. It's got a seat belt," said Fred.

Esther, seeing Fred's reluctance, grabbed the skateboard and rode it across the store, stopping with a fashionable 180-degree turn. She then turned to Fred and said, "See it's easy." Fred grimaced, but reluctantly grabbed the skateboard to give it a try.

Milo was watching. The store was closed, and his team was having some fun. Milo's risk monitor was already firing, talking to Milo's System 2 brain. "Hello, Milo, not sure a skateboard inside the store is a good idea. Hello, are you there?" Milo could clearly hear the voice. Yet, things were moving fast, and if he didn't want the skateboarding to continue, particularly if he didn't want Fred to get on that skateboard, he would have to quickly intervene.

Milo's risk monitor was not the only voice doing the talking, however. There was another voice, "Let 'em have some fun. Good team building." In retrospect, Milo was not sure where this voice came from. Milo knew his risk monitor as that background application – always running, but remaining silent unless it sees a risk. When it sees the risk, it knocks on the door of the System 2 brain, "Hello!" Milo even found that his risk monitor had a tone, an ability to modulate how loudly it yelled. If it were startled by a big risk, like the boy running into the street after the soccer ball, it would literally be screaming at him, "Danger! Warning!" If it was a little hazard, it might very well speak in a softer tone, "Hello, Milo, you just might wanna think about this." In this case of watching his team skateboarding in the store, his risk monitor was talking in a normal volume, as in "risk seen, but not a very large one," in comparison to "you are about to get hit by a bus."

The second voice, "Let 'em have some fun. Good team building," was new for Milo; he hadn't heard this voice since launching on this journey of human accountability. It was not some background application screaming at his System 2 brain, but instead it seemed that his System 2 brain was having a conversation with itself – or with his risk monitor. It was as if Milo himself, wherever "he" resided in his brain, was observing a debate. "I'm taking input on what I see in front of me. Anything to add before I make a decision?" Again, things were moving fast, and seeing no clear and convincing evidence that the shenanigans should be stopped, Milo decided to take a wait and see approach.

Fred grabbed the skateboard. Milo's System 2 brain, in what looked like a glaring inconsistency given its decision to take a wait and see approach to the scene unfolding before him, called out, "Be careful Fred." And now, for Milo, what happened in the next few seconds played out like a movie scene in slow motion. Milo could see Fred pushing off with his left foot, his right foot on the skateboard. Fred rolled across the store floor, slowly. Just a little faster than a walking pace, already recognizing what everyone there was about to learn. Fred had no idea how to stop. Learning to fly is learning to land, they tell aspiring pilots. Dock ramming is what new captains do when learning to pull their boats into port. In many parts of life, it's not the getting going that's the problem; it's the stopping. Fred probably knew this instinctually before he ever got on that skateboard.

As he approached the counter, Fred leaned back, his System 1 brain appearing to take over as if his lean would somehow act as a brake. New snow skiers do the same, leaning up the hill as if to defy gravity's relentless pull. Fred had momentum and that backward lean, and until he could push off against something, his momentum and that backward lean would keep him going – forward and downwards.

Instinctively, Esther called out "turn," as he approached the counter. Fred's lean had moved his center of gravity behind the rear wheels; the skateboard had now become a missile, propelled out from under his feet, shooting toward the oncoming counter. Fred's body was rotating around its center of mass, his head moving down, his feet moving up. For a split second, Fred was skateboarding horizontally, his arms whirling like windmills, his feet now up two feet off the ground…and then - he stopped.

Like a brick dropped from three feet up, Fred landed – hard - on his back. Gasping for breath, he groaned, "I think I broke a rib." Esther and Bryce stood for a moment, trying to control their laughter. Bryce looked at Fred and said, "Ok, not everyone can ride a skateboard!" Esther, her EMT training kicking in, dropped to one knee, "Stay still. Give it a moment. Breathe!"

Milo jumped in, "Listen to Esther." Fred complied. Currently struggling for breath, he wasn't going anywhere!

Esther poked and pushed gently around Fred's ribs. "Nothing broken, as far as I can tell. I think you're good to go. You're going to be a little bruised." A few minutes on the ground, his breath now caught, Fred stood up.

Nobody was saying much, just darting glances in Milo's direction to see what his response was going to be. "That," he said, his voice tinged with regret, "was really stupid."

Milo was kicking himself. That voice, his risk monitor, had called it correctly. Yet, his conscious brain had talked him out of saying anything. Faced with a choice to make, Milo made the wrong choice. Clearly, this required further analysis.

On the day after the skateboard event, Milo went golfing with his friend, John. John and Milo went to high school together, not great friends in high school, but had wound up living just a few miles apart as adults. John managed a local big-box retailer. Every six months or so, Milo and John played on a nine-hole executive course. That's the golf course for golfers who can't hit the ball very far. By the third hole, Milo was telling John about the previous day's skateboarding incident. As he related the story, Milo began to laugh as he recalled the sight of Fred's flailing arms just before he crashed "You should have seen it. This guy, Fred, is totally horizontal in the air. His arms were flailing around, looking for land," said Milo.

"And you just stood there?" said John.

"Well, yeah. What was I supposed to do at that point?" replied Milo.

"I'm not talking about when the guy was airborne," said John as he leaned over to put his ball on the tee. "I'm talking about when your other employees were egging this guy on."

For the next moment there was silence as John swung his 3-wood. "Crap," said John. "Did it again," referring to the slice to the right that always seemed to happen to him. "This is why I don't play a real course."

"So, yes, is the answer to your question," said Milo. "I did just stand there."

"Reckless," John said.

"What do you mean, reckless?" said Milo.

"Three of your employees riding a skateboard in your store, while you watch? That's reckless," said John.

"On my part or their part?" said Milo.

"Both, now that you ask. But I was focusing on you," said John as they dragged their golf bags down the fairway to the next hole. "You know, like reckless driving. For you it was just reckless managing," said John, swinging. "You said you just stood there, knowing their horseplay with the skateboard could get someone hurt or hurt the store," said John pulling a wedge from his bag and walking away from Milo toward his golf ball now sitting among the trees and weeds alongside the fairway. His final words, as he turned away from Milo … "That was reckless, buddy."

Milo's inquisitive mind was nothing if not tenacious. When a riddle invaded his consciousness, teasing him to find a solution, he wasn't likely to let it go. So it was with John's use of the word reckless.

Home from his golf game, Milo poured himself a lemonade, plunked down on the sofa in front of his widescreen TV, and flipped through the channels until he found a golf channel, hoping, perhaps, to learn something for his next round with John. Ever the multi-tasker, he opened his laptop as well, then his browser, then clicked his cursor over the search field, and typed the word "reckless."

Milo was impressed that John had but one word to describe his behavior around the skateboarding in the store. It did not take long for Milo to find what he was looking for, a reasonable definition of the word. "The conscious disregard of a substantial and unjustifiable risk," he read. Nine words, eight if he did not count the "the." He read them several times. Not much meaning at first, but it looked like he could unpack the definition if he looked at the individual words. "Conscious disregard," he said to himself. "I know what those words mean. That's Kahneman's System 2 brain, well, at least the 'conscious' part." He thought for a moment, "and the 'disregard,' that implies a choice. As if there was another path, a safer path, that was ignored."

It took Milo right back to that voice telling him that the skateboarding probably wasn't a great idea. Yet, there had been two voices competing with one another. One had told him that is was good team building, one had alerted him to a risk, and he had gone with the voice that told him "let them have some fun." Fun had value, too.

Milo thought he understood John's use of the word reckless. Milo saw the risk; his risk monitor fired, alerting his conscious System 2 brain to the hazard; yet, he had ignored the warning. To use John's definition, Milo "disregarded" the warning. In fact, he quite consciously disregarded the warning.

Milo turned his attention to the second part of the definition: a substantial and unjustifiable risk. Milo quickly understood the first part. "It must be a real risk, something of note," Milo said to himself.

The final part, "unjustifiable," needed further unpacking. There were clearly some risks in life that were necessary. Leaving your shelter to get food. In the modern world, having natural gas and 110 volts of electricity coursing through your home seemed to be necessary risks. The risk of a gas leak was outweighed by the benefit of being able to heat your home in the winter.

Milo grimaced as he thought, "Riding a skateboard in my store, *that* was unjustifiable."

Reckless was taking shape for Milo. It was not the human error - that slip, lapse or mistake as his professor friend, Ralph, had called it - filled with inadvertency. It was a choice, or the failure to make a choice, where to do so was to choose a knowingly unreasonable risk.

And importantly, it was not a subconscious choice. It had to be made in the conscious System 2 brain. A person's risk monitor would have to alert the conscious brain to the unjustifiable risk, and then, more importantly, the person would have to consciously *choose* to ignore it.

Reckless. No single word in the English language better described this behavior, other than the word "gambling," perhaps. Milo could see that in watching Fred pick up that skateboard, and not saying anything, not choosing to stop the skateboarding in the store, Milo was gambling with the store, and with Fred. Milo resisted having to apply that reckless label to himself – who willingly thinks of himself as reckless - yet, he knew why his golfing partner John used the term. Objectively, standing by as Fred skateboarded in the shop, regardless of the fun factor or potential for team building, looked pretty reckless.

MUNCHIES

Daniel's not really sure how he got off on this tangent. His mind had drifted to thinking about his employees not necessarily having the same values as him. Perhaps it was the guy in the pinstriped suit who believed that Esther should have continued making his sub while a critically injured person lay out on the street. It just hit him upside the head. Could it be possible that individual artisans did not share the same values as Dave's Subs? It was a question now haunting Daniel. Do we stand in judgment of employees through the values of the organization? Is that justice?

For Daniel it was easy to see the mission and values of Dave's Subs. It was a for profit company. It would exist to provide value for its shareholders, in this case being Dave and his family. It would exist for its customers, to fill a market need for good lunch food, with fast and friendly service. It would exist to be a good place to work for its employees. And finally it would try to be a good citizen within its community, being green, providing value to the community with the least possible environmental footprint. It would additionally try to give back, as it did providing free subs for junior and senior high school functions throughout the year.

Now, mapping employees into that framework was more difficult. Not every employee had the same ideas about shareholder return or what role Dave's Subs should play in the community. Bluntly, if a sub artisan would rather be an offshore fisherman, it was not Dave's responsibility to retool his sub chain to align with an employee's offshore fishing aspirations. Some questions were settled. Dave's was a sub shop. Locally grown food, fast and friendly service. That was its market position. And until something radical changed in the environment, or until it was impossibly unprofitable, it would remain a sub shop.

Employees, in Daniel's mind, were not so settled. In fact, most of Daniel's artisans were on their way to somewhere else. Dave's Subs was not the destination, and Daniel knew that. Every artisan had their own mission, their own values. And this was important for Daniel to recognize. To be a good manager was to understand what motivated his employees.

Daniel would work to build a simplified model of his employees, and it would start with the Declaration of Independence. Daniel had always been a fan of Thomas Jefferson. As an artist, he could appreciate how much meaning and eloquence could be put into a very small number of words. In the declaration, Jefferson wrote that we were all

"Endowed by our Creator with certain unalienable rights, among these life, liberty, and the pursuit of happiness."

There was, to Daniel, much wisdom packed into these last seven words. Life, liberty, and the pursuit of happiness. The latter spoke to the mission of every human being. Happiness would not be encoded in us. If we wanted to be miserable, that was our right. Yet, in perhaps very simplified form, the pursuit of happiness could very well be seen as the mission of every human being. What is it we seek? In a word, happiness.

The importance of life goes without saying. Liberty – that is, the freedom to exercise our free will in a manner suiting our happiness – free from intrusion.

Missions, whether individual or corporate, take the form of pursuits. What is it we want to be in the world? Daniel could identify four markers in his life that tied specifically to his pursuit of happiness. They were peace, love, joy, and purpose. The first three were easy for Daniel: Music, his home, his wife, they gave Daniel peace. Daniel loved, and was loved by, his wife, his girls, his family and friends. Joy, those too were tied to his family and friends.

The fourth tied to the purpose Daniel had in his life – what choices did he make that furthered his sense of life purpose? For Daniel, it was his music that made the difference. Making music himself, teaching his young students, that was purpose: his music was adding to life. Life, liberty, and the pursuit of happiness. Peace, love, joy and purpose.

This was not new ground for Daniel – those four words were etched on a piece of glass, framed on his bathroom wall, close to the mirror. Daniel would wake up every morning, seeing these words as he brushed his teeth. Daniel would think about his day. What, in that day to come, would give Daniel peace, love, joy, and purpose? It kept him centered. That was Daniel, and in his mind to some extent, every one of us.

Daniel knew there was a flip side to the coin. Perhaps a bit more self-centered. Protective, rather than pursuing. It was our movement through life, collecting things. Assets. Property. We all seek them out during our lifetime. With them comes power and influence. With them comes the ability to control our own destiny. Knowledge, skill, wealth, fitness, reputation, autonomy, belonging, fairness. People hold on to these as if they were all tangible property.

Daniel knew it was a pretty simplistic view of human motivation. Yet, it worked. Humans, in their individual pursuit of peace, love, joy and purpose were clearly self-centered. Every man for himself; every woman for herself. Daniel didn't find this idea necessarily negative. Just that as individuals, we think as individuals. When it came to understanding human motivation, understanding that individuals thought individually, it seemed to have a big application pay-off when one was tasked with managing those same humans.

About 60 days into their new jobs, Charles noticed that a few of the artisans had all adopted a habit of sneaking into the walk-in refrigerator and nibbling on sandwich meats and cheeses. It was subtle, and kept out of Daniel's field of view, as Dave's Subs had a policy that employees were required to purchase food as customers. There were no "complimentary" meals for employees at Dave's Subs.

Charles took the initiative. He caught Daniel after everyone else had left for the day. "Daniel, I need to talk to you about something," said Charles.

"Yeah, what is it?" replied Daniel.

"I think some of your team has a case of the munchies," said Charles. "Some of the team is munching on food in the walk-in."

"Who?" asked Daniel.

"I'd rather not say," replied Charles.

"OK," said Daniel.

"You have young employees going to college. Spending money on food is hard for them. They're working around food and they're hungry. It happens in shops like this," said Charles. "Not justifying it. Just saying..."

It struck Daniel as odd that Charles would be so tolerant of team members sneaking food from the walk-in. "What would you do?" asked Daniel.

"I'd comp them a meal," said Charles.

"But they're stealing food," replied Daniel.

"And it happens at every restaurant. It's hard for humans to work around food and not want to eat some of it," said Charles. "Giving employees a sub and soda for a four hour shift will make your employees happy, and that will make for happy customers."

"Yeah," said Daniel. "I see your point."

Daniel thanked Charles for coming forward and reporting what he had seen. Charles was a good guy. He was having trouble meeting the subs per rush minimum, but he was a good guy, someone Daniel could rely on to make good choices at the store.

As a manager, Daniel again found himself within that intellectual space between systems and the humans tasked to work within them. Was the stealing from the refrigerator a "system" problem, or was it an "employee" problem? Daniel let that question go. It was a problem, and Charles offered a reasonable solution.

Based upon Charles's proposal, Daniel got approval from Dave to add a "comp" policy to provide one sub and one drink "complimentary" for any shift more than four hours. It was a hit with the team. Making what they did, the artisans surely didn't want to spend an hour's earnings on a sub. It was a good, and reasonable, benefit for the team.

Charles did let Daniel know that the new policy appeared to have eliminated the "sneaking" behavior, and was well appreciated by the younger members of the team.

NICE GUYS FINISH LAST

Charles is a genuinely nice guy. To watch him make subs is to watch him warmly engage each and every customer. Charles made it a point to find something cheery to say to each customer who came across his station. If he saw a book they were carrying, he'd ask them how they liked it. If they were wearing running clothes, he'd ask if they were a runner, and then would ask where they ran. Charles took a personal interest in every customer.

Milo began to believe this was part of Charles' problem with speed. Now Milo didn't believe that Charles would ever produce subs as fast as Esther or Alisha. They simply hustled – they were focused and efficient. And that was mainly what the customers at Dave's Subs appreciated. They liked Charles; they just liked having more time to eat their lunch more.

Milo had identified several opportunities for Charles to improve his sub production rate. It was, after all, a core measure for Dave's Subs employees. It meant, effectively, that Charles would have to put more energy into speed and a little less interest in getting to know each customer.

"Charles, do you have a few minutes to talk?" Milo asked Charles at the end of his shift.

"Sure. What's it about?" asked Charles.

"I just want to talk to you about your work as an artisan," said Milo.

They sat down at one of the tables. The other artisans had already wrapped up their work and left the store, allowing Charles and Milo to speak privately.

"Charles, you know that we track artisan speed?" said Milo.

"Yeah. And how am I doing?" asked Charles.

"You're just a bit under the minimum of 60 subs per 90 minute rush. You're at 53 subs per rush," said Milo.

"What's that mean for me?" asked Charles. "Is my job in jeopardy?"

"Charles, I need to get you up over that 60 mark. And I think I can get you there," said Milo.

"How? What can I do?" asked Charles.

"It's simple. I just need you to focus a bit more on speed, a little less on conversation while you're tending to your customers. At Dave's Subs, we have two competing values – fast *and* friendly. Our customers value both. I just need you to tilt a little more toward speed," said Milo.

"I get it," said Charles. "Can I ask what a top performer does here at Dave's Subs?"

"Charles, here and at Dave's original store we have artisans that can do 80-90 subs per rush," said Milo.

"Wow!" said Charles, genuinely impressed. "So I need to do more than just 60 subs per rush?"

"I need you to get where you can get," said Milo. "You don't need to be the fastest artisan. I just need you to be as fast as you can be. You should be able to get close to 70 subs per rush."

"Milo, I'll work it. You know I will," said Charles. "Thank you for talking to me."

"Charles, I want you to remain friendly to our customers," said Milo. "You're a great artisan. I just need you to put a bit more focus on speed during the lunch rush."

"I will," said Charles. "Thank you."

Milo watched Charles over the next several weeks. And his subs/rush number moved up from 53 to 62. His conversation had worked. Charles was a bit more focused on the task at hand - getting a completed sub to his customers. Importantly, no customers seemed to notice or mind the small decrease in conversation with Charles.

Milo didn't know how long Charles would be able to keep it up. A lunch rush at Dave's Subs was not for everyone. During those 90 minutes, artisans were really hustling to get food out the door. It was like a workout – physically demanding, yet social at the same time. Nonetheless, Milo appreciated Charles for being so responsive to his coaching.

It led Milo back once again to the systems versus employees debate that had been swirling around his head. Milo had watched, both at Dave's Subs and at previous employers, how management decisions seem to be made. Managers would get caught in this binary decision-making process. When bad things happened, managers would ask if it was the system or the employee's fault. And that word itself, "fault," was beginning to bother Milo. To him, it was not about finding fault.

It was about understanding the relationship between humans and the systems in which they operate. Milo could think about Dave's day at the track, and the outright stupid design at Pablo's of orders being taken, and then hand written again to give to runners who took those orders back to the kitchen. Milo recalled Dave's comment that humans could not overcome really bad system design.

Yet, at the other end of the scale, was the task of assembling subs in what Milo and Dave believed to be a reasonable system. It took hustle during the lunch hour, and the difference between artisans seemed less about systems and more about individual hustle. Milo could see it in sports – some players just worked harder and smarter than others. Milo could see it in his artisans. Esther and Alisha, for whatever reason, were simply determined to push out subs.

Milo did know that if he focused too much on production, his artisans were likely to begin undervaluing other things, like good hygiene or friendliness. But as long as Milo kept watch on those, he felt safe in pushing production. After all, that's why Milo hired his artisans – to produce subs.

Uncle Julio

Milo continued tinkering with his model, particularly as he watched the evening news, the place where the newscasters lined up people for viewers to judge. It was almost a national sport, passing judgment on the choices other people made. A bank robber. A politician making an off the books deal to secure votes. The drive-by shooter of a shop owner. Newscasters teed them up sequentially by the amount of blood involved so viewers could be increasingly appalled at what their fellow human beings were capable of.

Quickly, though, Milo encountered the limits of his new word. Reckless seemed inadequate to describe what he saw on the evening news. "Bank robbery. Drive-by shooting, buying votes...these aren't reckless behaviors; they're criminal. These all have laws written specifically to address them," Milo thought to himself. Clearly, there was an extreme end of the continuum from human error where something happens that is other than what was intended, and knowingly or intentionally choosing to rob a bank, or heading out with the purpose of participating in a drive-by shooting.

Unless a person had mental issues, Milo thought, they would have to know that harm was absolutely going to occur in a bank robbery, or in a drive-by shooting, or even in a vote-buying scheme. These were examples of somebody saying, "I'm going to take what does not belong to me" whether it was somebody's life or somebody's property.

Milo realized that the word "reckless" was much more subtle. It wasn't a word about *knowingly* taking from or harming another, nor was it a word about *inadvertently* taking or harming another. Rather, it seemed to stand right there in the middle. It was the gamble. It was the decision to gamble with other people's stuff.

And Milo had a prime example of reckless seared indelibly into his heart and mind. It was Uncle Julio. When Milo was a teenager, his Uncle Julio had been involved in an auto accident. Intoxicated, he'd attempted to merge onto the freeway using the exit ramp instead of the on-ramp. There he was, driving down the ramp when a loaded school bus was coming off of the freeway, up the ramp, heading right toward Uncle Julio.

Uncle Julio didn't kill any of the kids on the bus that day. The bus driver laid on the horn, and at the last moment, even through the alcohol haze, it appeared Julio's risk monitor fired. Hearing the horn or seeing the big yellow bus in front of him, Uncle Julio turned the wheel hard toward the embankment heading down toward the freeway, his right front tire hitting the curb, pushing the car into the air, causing it to tumble down the embankment but stopping before the rush of oncoming traffic. All caught on

Department of Transportation video. Uncle Julio was a bit scraped up, the bus driver shaken, but the children unharmed.

In the end, Uncle Julio was charged and convicted of DUI, his third conviction in seven years. He spent three years in the state prison and came out a broken and bitter man. At some level, Uncle Julio thought his punishment had been unfair. Three years in jail had cost him everything — his job, his marriage, his children, his extended family. In his mind, he hadn't hurt anybody; in fact, he figured he'd done a great job of avoiding hurting those kids considering how drunk he was. Even drunk, part of him thought, he drove better and with more skill than half the population driving on the road.

Uncle Julio meant no harm to those kids on the bus, or to the bus driver. He was just trying to get home from an afternoon with friends at the local pub. He was just trying to get through life, in the way that was Uncle Julio. Yet, Milo knew, his uncle had recklessly endangered the lives of every one of those children, the life of the bus driver, Uncle Julio's own life, and the life of anybody with the bad luck of driving in the vicinity of Uncle Julio on that afternoon. He had gambled with the lives of all of those people, and for that, Milo thought his punishment fit the crime.

Milo's extended family was about equally split in how they viewed Uncle Julio's imprisonment. Some saw Uncle Julio's three years in jail as excessive given he didn't kill anyone, while others thought he got off light because of the risk he took with that entire busload of children. Bottom line, talking about Uncle Julio was itself reckless for the family brawl that ensued.

Being reckless was the zone in the middle, not human error, but not with the intent to harm either. Uncle Julio didn't leave work on that afternoon and intend to harm a busload of children or anyone else. He was a great guy who loved children and loved to have fun. But in choosing to drink after work with his buddies and then get into his car and drive home, Uncle Julio chose to gamble with all those lives. And it was his choice to gamble that led to his incarceration and family condemnation. For Uncle Julio it came with three years in jail. For Milo's family it came with shame, that an Alvarez would be willing to put a group of kids on a school bus in harm's way. And that's why Milo's family chose not to talk about it.

Milo's father was deeply religious. He would often say to Milo and his siblings, "God gave you free will. How you gonna use it?" Milo didn't know if that was a reflection of his father's angst about Uncle Julio. For Milo's father, every human being had to make choices. Some big – don't rob a bank, don't abuse your wife and children, don't drive drunk – some less big – which college to attend, blue shirt or red.

Reckless or benign choices. Recognize the risk of harm but disregard that awareness and take the gamble anyway. When a person sees that gamble, sees it as unjustifiable, but chooses to do it anyway, they became Uncle Julio.

Had Milo become Uncle Julio by standing back and not taking action when his team was egging Fred on in the skateboarding incident inside the store? Milo could see this wasn't the same order of magnitude as Uncle Julio's drunk driving. Yet, out on the golf course, John had, without hesitation, labeled his decision reckless. Milo was gambling with Fred and with the store. There had been no reason to take the risk. Milo's risk monitor had alerted him to the risk, to the point where he felt he had two voices, one perched on each shoulder, jibber jabbering in his ears, while he – and they, the voices - watched the antics unfold. The magnitude of the potential harm may be different, but that didn't change the label, only the penalty that followed. For Uncle Julio, it was jail time. For Milo, well, at this point, only the gentle ribbing of a golfing partner.

PANTOPHOBIA

There is a famous scene in *A Charlie Brown Christmas* where Charlie Brown visits Lucy's psychiatric help desk. It's out in the snow, unattended until Charlie Brown shows up. Schroeder, talking to Lucy nearby says, "I think you have a customer." Lucy quickly mans the psychiatric help stand, pushing off the snow that had accumulated, and turns around the sign to read, "The Doctor is Real In."

Lucy asks, "May I help you?"

Charlie responds, "I am in sad shape."

That was all it took. Lucy knows she has a real customer. She reaches under the counter and pulls out a tin jar. "Wait a minute, before you begin, I must ask that you pay in advance. Five cents please." Charlie Brown, without saying anything, reaches into his pocket and pulls out what appears to be his only coin, and puts it in the tin jar. Lucy launches into a monologue on the joys of capitalism, shaking the tin jar, ranting about how much she likes the sound of money. "Nickels, nickels, nickels," she joyfully exclaims. "All right now, what seems to be your trouble?" she finally asks the hapless Charlie Brown.

"I feel depressed. I know I should be happy, but I'm not," says Charlie Brown.

"As they say on TV, the mere fact that you realize you need help indicates that you are not too far gone," says Lucy. "I think we better pinpoint your fears. If we can find out what you're afraid of, we can label it."

Milo felt like Charlie Brown. He was well down the road of labeling behaviors, those of his team, and occasionally, as in the case of the skateboarding event, his own behaviors. Just as Lucy had a label for Charlie Brown – Pantophobia - Milo now had labels he could use to describe the human behaviors he witnessed around him.

Milo knew that the labels were important because that's where his journey had begun. That letter from Dave in reaction to Alisha's event. Those words, "We will not fire an employee simply because they have made a mistake," documented for every employee to see. Those words created an expectation. Dave's Subs will not fire an employee simply because they made a mistake. Those words had importance. For Milo though, they had lacked meaning. Well, at least that last word, "mistake." Now Milo could distinguish human error from reckless. And, of course, there were those choices made, seemingly by System 1, which sat in between mistakes and reckless choices. Bringing definition, and labels, to those would come later for Milo.

Dave's letter had made it clear that there was a link between the labels and whether someone was going to get whacked. "We will not fire an employee simply because they have made a mistake," meant that Dave was putting a limitation on his right to disciplinary sanction. Sanction would follow from some labels, not others. And this led Milo to think more clearly about discipline. Under what circumstances would Milo use discipline? And for what reason?

Milo sat watching golf on TV, again, while his wife, Isabel, put his two 6-year old daughters to bed. Isabel came out of the girl's bedroom to see Milo on the sofa, staring off into space, clearly not paying any attention to the golf program. "What are you thinking about, honey?" asked Isabel.

"Punishment," responded Milo.

"Why that?"

"I have to define what it means for Dave's Subs," said Dave.

"And we have to define what it means as parents for our two girls," said Isabel.

"So, what does it mean to you?" asked Milo.

"I dunno. I suppose, in a nutshell, it's about consequences for our actions," said Isabel. "We all have to be accountable for our actions."

"Easy to say, but what does that mean?" asked Milo.

"If you do something bad, you face the consequences," said Isabel.

"And what about Alisha? We said we would not terminate an employee for a simple human mistake," said Milo.

"What consequence could Alisha face that would change anything that happened?" asked Isabel. "Would punishing Alisha have erased the harm to Ms. Foster? Would it make Alisha a better employee? And you know, if you'd stopped there at firing Alisha that would have ended it right there. You certainly wouldn't have gone on this journey to figure out what makes a just workplace…and frankly, I think the work you're doing, your struggles to figure this stuff out, is noble. I'm proud of you!"

Milo looked at his wife. "This," he thought, "is why I married this woman. She always encourages my sometimes wacky ideas – and often takes the journey with me."

"No, punishing Alisha would not have changed a thing," said Milo. And with that, he kissed Isabel on the forehead, called it a night, and went to bed dreaming about punishment.

He awoke about 3:30 in the morning, the details about his dream hazy. But he had figured it out. "Punishment is danger. The threat of punishment is artificial danger. It's a man-made consequence," Milo thought to himself. He knew he wouldn't be able to get back to sleep. He was up for the day. He grabbed a post-it note by his bed and wrote, "Punishment is Danger," and then headed to have a shower.

In the shower, where much of our best thinking occurs, it came back to him, what he'd been dreaming about. It was related to a previous conversation he'd had with Isabel several years earlier.

Like many new parents, Isabel and Milo read more than a few parenting books, and had more than a few parenting discussions, with varying degrees of heat. What Milo was remembering, and dreaming about, was the discussion they'd had about consequences. Isabel had read a book, or maybe it was an article, about "natural consequences" as a parenting tool. It was a perennial topic in parenting circles. "Let your children see the natural consequences of their behavior," the professionals said.

Standing there in the shower, Milo remembered how unsettled he'd been with the discussion. Isabel was advocating what the professionals were saying, "We need to let our daughters see the natural consequences of their actions," Isabel had said. "They need to learn about the world around them."

It didn't sit well with Milo, especially now with the hindsight of Alisha's event. Patti Foster suffered the natural consequences of Alisha's mistake. She ended up in the hospital for three days and missed not only a trip to Hawaii, but her only child's wedding. But to have terminated Alisha would not have been a natural consequence; it was artificial. Milo and Dave would have had to impose it. Nothing about it was natural, unless whacking people for bad outcomes was simply the natural order of things. Ultimately, Dave's letter and what Milo was coming to firmly believe, was that whacking people for making a mistake should not be part of the natural order.

Milo thought more about natural consequences. Natural consequences seemed to refer to the consequences that naturally flow from a particular set of behaviors. That much Milo understood. Touch a hot stove, get burned. *That* is a natural consequence.

On the other hand, if one of his 6-year old daughters left an empty potato chip bag on the floor of her bedroom, the natural consequences might result in ants crawling up the outside of the house and through her window just to get at the scraps inside the bag. The natural consequence comes with a bit of cleanup. But until the ants arrive, *if* they arrive, Milo's daughter just might not see or believe that ants will scale the outside wall of her house to get at the forgotten potato chip bag.

This was the essence of his natural consequences discussion with Isabel. Isabel was saying that if the girls did not put away their toys, they should be prohibited from using them the next day. "Natural consequences," Isabel said as if that foreclosed any further discussion.

"Seems logical, but not very natural," Milo remembered responding. "Actually, not putting them away just means that the toys will be easier to play with tomorrow," Milo added.

It is at that point, he remembered Isabel giving him that look, and saying "you just don't understand," as she walked away down the hallway, taking the toys with her.

His mind, better served back with the potato chips bag, could see that most parents were constitutionally incapable of waiting for the natural consequence of the ants' arrival. Parents felt compelled to create a penalty for leaving opened potato chip bags in a bedroom *in anticipation* of the *potential* natural consequences. Some would even create penalties for taking potato chip bags *into* a bedroom in anticipation that the bag would not be thrown out. And, of course, some parents would not even buy potato chips. It became clear to Milo that parents created artificial danger to encourage desired behavior.

With his own girls, Milo told them, "If I find empty potato chip bags in your room, it will be you who cleans the kitchen," Milo had said, wagging his index finger at them for emphasis.

"Tough language for six year old girls," Isabel had muttered under her breath.

"At least the consequences are food related!" he'd retorted. It seemed the conversation must have ended there, as Milo couldn't remember anything further about it...

Milo was beginning to see that, by definition, artificial danger had absolutely no rational relation to the hazard created; that's what made it artificial. Natural consequences are a wonderful, and often memorable, teacher. Hand in fire, burnt hand. Yet, when they are not available, or when irreparable harm is the natural consequence, we need alternative means to encouraging the right behavior. Artificial consequences are the ones we create to add risk, to help a human choose a different path, in recognition of the artificial danger. "If natural consequences work, Milo thought, let them work. If they don't, resort to using artificial consequences."

His dream tied right back to Milo's risk monitor. Put his hands in the fire, it taught his risk monitor that fire is hot and can hurt. The next time he was around fire, his risk monitor would go off, and unless he was a real adrenaline junky, he'd keep a healthy distance from the fire. For a child, though, leaving a potato chip bag in a room does nothing to teach that child's risk monitor about the hazards of the behavior, until the ants arrive. For most homeowners, that's too late. They now have an ant infestation. Best to address it before the ants arrive. Hence, the artificial danger.

A picture of punishment was coming into view, frustrating Milo that it took him into his 30's to see clearly what was going on. Whether in the workplace, at home, or on the streets, humans created rules for family, employees, and citizens to follow. Milo made work rules, and he expected his artisans to follow them. Yet, making a rule was not enough. Rules are not danger in *themselves*, Milo had quickly deduced.

The teenager who thinks he won't get caught texting and driving, or the business executive who thinks nobody will notice the adjustments he's entered in the accounting system are part of our collective focus on consequences rather than on the rules. The truth, for the teenager and the business executive is that they probably could get away with breaking the rules – for a time and possibly with some real benefit – for them. Milo, who occasionally drove faster than the speed limit, knew that's why he reacted more to the police officer parked ahead – foot immediately taps brakes - than to the speed limit sign itself. The sign represented a rule, the police officer the threat of a consequence.

To work effectively, rules needed consequences, the more immediate the better. And that was where artificial danger came in. If an individual risk monitor did not see the risks inherent in a behavior, employers, parents, or the state needed to create enough artificial danger to get that risk monitor to fire.

Milo was adding an important piece to his model: punishment was about the threat of artificial danger. We discipline, to varying degrees, conduct that we find unacceptable. Milo's daughter might not see that natural consequence of the ants, principally because her lesson was too expensive for Milo, but she surely saw the pain in cleaning the kitchen floor, especially as a six-year old. For Milo, that was the theory. Where natural consequences did not work, or the natural consequences were just too dire to experience, we would create artificial consequences to deter the commission of the offense.

None of Your Business

Milo loves sports. He watched the American big three intently: football, basketball, and baseball. Of particular interest was the off-hours conduct of players. Milo got much of his information by reading the Yahoo app on his phone. It was his one voyeuristic indulgence, a treasure trove of athletic and celebrity off-hours conduct. Professional sports stars carrying guns into nightclubs, getting in public fights with spouses, pushing and shoving paparazzi. And of course, there was that all important question, "Who was one of his favorites now dating?"

The dialogue in the press about conduct off the field always intrigued Milo. A football player assaults his wife. A basketball player gets caught stealing from a department store. A baseball player gets convicted of drunk driving. Milo found himself paying increased attention to these stories, in part because of his exploration of workplace justice. Each time a sports star got into trouble, Milo wondered what action their employer, or the team, should take. Central to Milo's thought were the questions: what role did the team play, and what role did the state play? If a player got convicted of drunk driving, was that an issue for the state or for the team? Milo himself was conflicted. Not so the press. Not so the general public it seemed. And that's precisely what bothered Milo.

It was not an easy question. For Milo, at a very simple level, what happened off-hours was not related to work. What happened on-hours, that was his business. It was not that Milo didn't care; it was that he respected the privacy of his artisans' off-hours lives. If one of his artisans was convicted of drunk driving on Saturday, but could somehow show up to work on Monday, that was good enough for him. Milo believed that as long as their on-hours work was going well, what they did off hours was their business.

The call came about 10:00 a.m. one fall Monday morning. It came from Charles's wife, Beverly. Milo had met Beverly at a company dinner function. They had probably shared 50 words. Charles was a private individual, which meant most of his peers at Dave's Subs did not know much of his personal life.

"Milo?" she asked. "Is this Milo?" Her voice was sheepish, and she sounded upset.

"Yes, this is Milo."

"This is Beverly, Charles's wife."

"Hello there Mrs. Stuart," Milo said deferentially.

Milo knew something was wrong. Charles was supposed to be at work at 10:30. He was already an hour late, and he hadn't answered his phone when Milo had tried to give him a call at 11:00.

Milo thought the worst. Perhaps Charles had a medical problem, maybe it was a heart attack, Milo thought revealing some ageism. Charles was old, at least relative to Milo. Surely, it had to be a health issue. Was he in the hospital? Was he dead? Whatever the cause, Milo's System 2 brain immediately headed to the worst possible conclusion.

"Milo, Charles is not going to make it into work today," she said.

Confirmation for Milo that Charles did have a health event.

"I'm so ashamed," she said.

That caught Milo off guard.

She continued. "Milo, Charles is at the hospital. And when he's checked out there, he's on his way to jail."

"What?" said Milo, totally lost at this point.

"Charles was at a rally early this morning. More of a protest, I guess. At the state house. You remember that he's a teacher. Well, he was there with about another 100 people who were protesting planned reductions in school lunch programs."

"So how does that lead him to the hospital and jail?" interjected Milo.

"The protesters blocked the doors to the house chamber. Maybe it was Charles growing up in the 60's. It just seemed to him like the right thing to do. Anyway, they kept the legislators from entering through the front door. Police were there and physically had to remove the protestors," said Beverly.

"One of the other protesters, from what Charles said older than him, started a bit of a brawl with one of the police officers who was trying to physically remove them."

"It turned into a fight?" said Milo, now totally taken aback.

"Yes, it's on the daytime news. Honestly, this was just supposed to be bunch of retired teachers protesting for the children. What harm could they cause?" she asked.

"Don't worry, Mrs. Stuart. It'll be ok," said Milo.

"Charles is being charged with assault of a police officer," she said.

"What?" said Milo, feeling like, perhaps, things weren't going to be ok.

"Charles tried to restrain the other protester, Bob, who he's known for 20 years. Bob just let his advocacy get out of control. Charles said he was pulling him away from the police officer when Charles's arm slipped, from the force of the pull. As his arm slipped, he elbowed another officer in the face. Broke his nose, from what Charles said. And the reason Charles is at the hospital, it looks like he might have fractured or displaced a bone in his elbow. He's quite sore," Beverly finished in a rush.

"Wow. Ok. I get it," Milo paused. "Charles is the last person I would ever expect to get mixed up in a thing like this, Mrs. Stuart. He's so kind and gentle.

"I know. He's so upset at himself. He'll probably spend the afternoon getting processed at jail. Assaulting an officer is a felony, but Charles thinks the facts of the event and the fact that they are a bunch of geriatric teachers looks good for them.

But Milo, Charles is being told his arm will be in a sling for much of this week. So, really, he's gonna have to miss a week of work. I am so sorry for this. I am so ashamed," she said quietly.

"Mrs. Stuart, you have no reason to be ashamed," said Milo. "And neither does Charles. He stood up for what he believed.

And I'm sure he did not intend to elbow that police officer. I'm sure it's going to be ok once this all gets sorted out."

Charles showed up to work the next week, on Monday, at 10:30 am. Alisha, Esther, and Bryce were there before Charles arrived. As he walked through the door, they began to clap. Charles was taken aback. He was both embarrassed and pleased by their reaction. Pleased by his fellow artisans acknowledgment that he and his fellow retired teachers had done a good deed, embarrassed and self-conscious about being the center of attention. Even Milo joined in the applause.

For Milo, it was a chance to think about the off-hour conduct of his employees. Charles had been charged with a felony, although the charge was dropped pretty quickly. Charles missed a week of work. The legislature rethought its position on school lunch funding.

"Was Charles's lost week an unexcused absence?" Milo thought to himself. Yes, if he followed his own rules. Yet, Milo let the absence slide. Was it Milo's business what Charles did outside of work? Milo concluded that what was important for him was what his employees did on the job. Yes, there are certain jobs where conduct outside of work is a reliable indicator of how an employee might act on the job. A psychiatrist convicted of child molestation off of work surely impacts the employability of the psychiatrist. An accountant who embezzles from her church outside of work probably tells us something of the accountant's trustworthiness at work.

Milo felt strongly, however, that it was not his job to judge the outside conduct. He was not judge and jury. It was not up to Milo to investigate the assault charge. That was up to the police and the courts. For conduct outside of work, it was up to the state to make the call.

Charles behavior did impact the store. He did not call in on that first day he missed. He did not find an artisan to cover his shift. And, he missed the rest of that week. Like any employee missing work, the absence mattered because of the hardship it placed on others. And short of an excused absence, it counted against Charles. It was to be part of the picture of what was Charles's work performance.

Slicing Beef

Dave stopped by the store to see how things were going. It was Friday afternoon, just an hour or so before the store was set to close and an opportunity for Milo to catch up on the buzz from other stores. Dave had recently moved a long-time employee, Robin, into his role as manager of Store #1, the original Dave's Subs.

"We had a pretty bad injury at the Woodbridge store. A relatively new artisan was helping Robin prep roast beef, using the meat slicer. She cut her hand when she was cleaning the slicer," said Dave.

"How bad?" asked Milo.

"Fourteen stitches," said Dave.

"Ouch. How did it happen?" asked Milo.

"I just told you," said Dave quizzically. "She cut her hand on the meat slicer," he repeated.

Milo's exploration into accountability was leading him to the recognition that it was tough to hold people accountable if you didn't dig deep behind the cause or causes of an event. For Dave, the artisan's cut hand was caused by her interaction with the slicer. Meat slicer meet artisan. Yes, Dave had instructed all of his stores to ensure that new artisans were properly trained on the use of the meat slicer. But for Milo, that was not enough. The term "causality" was about the science of cause and effect relationships, and the different biases people brought to their understanding of causes and their effects. An toddler's dish hits the floor; the scientist explains it by gravity, the mother by the fact that the infant pushed it off of the tray. Different people often saw the same event through very different eyes.

Milo knew that human beings would make mistakes. That was the start of this entire journey. That said, Milo now knew there was much more to the story. Milo would read the headline of an aircraft accident report: pilot error. He would see the headline of someone killed in a hospital: medical error. Those explanations were now growing old and tired. Milo wanted more. Yes, humans make mistakes. Now, surely we could move beyond that?

Milo wanted to understand why a particular error occurred. If a pilot made a mistake, the next step was to understand *why* the pilot made the mistake. If a surgeon or nurse made a mistake, *why* did they make a mistake? Milo could see that behind every event we cast as human error, there was a story. And if we were to fix any of these, we would need to look at the story's details, those less visible systems and the behaviors that might have led to the very visible error. It was as if the bad outcome and its immediate error were so bright that it was hard to see anything else, like the poorly designed system or the bad behavioral choice of the human being within that system who ultimately caused the error. And if Milo couldn't see the things that contributed to the error, he knew he'd never be able to learn from it, or come up with strategies to lessen the likelihood of it happening again.

The artisan's cut hand bothered Milo for the entire weekend. It was not an artisan from his store, but it was a human being who needed 14 stitches. Milo saw a potential learning opportunity for himself and the artisans at his store. Did the artisan at the other store do anything that might have led to her cut hand? Was there something about that particular meat slicer that made it particularly dangerous? Did that artisan do something that increased the likelihood of cutting her hand? Milo could not let it go. It gnawed at him until finally, he called Dave.

"Dave, this is Milo."

"What's up?"

"I've been thinking of our Friday conversation. About the artisan who cut her hand," said Milo.

"And?" said Dave, knowing that Milo was searching for something.

"I'd like to suggest that we do more to understand what happened," said Milo. "I know that we're going to make sure that every artisan using the machine goes through training."

"Isn't that enough?" asked Dave.

"No," said Milo. "We need more. We need to understand why the event occurred. Look, you're going to spend time and money on training and re-training your employees and yet, when it's all done, you still won't know if the training would have prevented that artisan's injury. Nor will you be in any better position to minimize the risk that a similar injury happens again. You've already trained your artisans to be careful. Retraining them to be more careful doesn't strike me as particularly helpful."

"I thought Robin did the investigation," Dave said meekly.

"She did. But I'm guessing not deep enough," said Milo. "Behind every error is the system, the environment that an employee works within. And included in every system we design will be the choices of our artisans. To understand this event, our artisan's cut hand, we need to dig deep, behind the error, to the systems and behaviors that led to the event."

"So what would you have me do?" asked Dave.

"Ask Robin to talk to the artisan again, if she hasn't already. I mean really talk to her. Listen to her story. Ask her to take Robin through her process, no detail left out. Did anything in the system, and I guess, in this case, we're talking about the slicer itself and our instructions for its use, did anything there contribute to this event? And then, look at her choices. She might not remember what she did in this particular case, but she could surely explain how she normally cleans the slicer. Watch what she does. See if there is anything in her technique that could have contributed to her sliced hand. It's not about pointing a finger; it's about learning. It's about giving others the chance to learn from her mistake. It's about the chance to truly prevent this from happening again."

"Ok, Milo, I'll talk with Robin. You know this exploration of yours is really changing your view of the world. And so far, I like it," said Dave.

Milo knew this journey was pushing him out on a fringe in the management world. For now, Dave was giving him some rope, letting Milo explore his new set of ideas.

About a week later, Dave called Milo. "Milo, I wanted to give you a call. I just got the briefing from Robin."

"What did she say?" asked Milo.

"She investigated, as you suggested. Now, she doesn't have your knowledge of these ideas like you. She did find some interesting things, though. The artisan, Lisa, was new to the equipment. She had a wet rag in her hand, cleaning up after she and Robin had finished slicing the roast beef. The slicer itself has a sharpener mounted on it, sitting underneath a polished stainless steel hood. Now, she wasn't sharpening the blade. But she did open the hood over the sharpening wheels in order to clean it. The hood measured probably five inches long and three inches high and wide. It covered two polishing wheels. Anyway, she opened the hood to clean around that part of the slicer. The hinge supporting that hood was filled with a bit of gunk, probably food parts. It made the hood hard to open and close. Opening it, the artisan could reach underneath the hood, grabbing its open edge. To close it, however, required that the artisan push on its rounded, polished top. There was no handle, only the shiny, slick polished hood. Her hands were slippery from the wet rag, it required a lot of force because of the gunked up hinge, and her hand slipped. If you look at the design of the slicer, if you are pushing on that hood and your hand slips, it goes right into the end of the blade. It was a bit of an accident waiting to happen."

"Wow," said Milo.

"You're right," said Dave.

"So do you still think training is the answer?" said Milo.

"Well, not entirely, if at all. Robin suggested we make sure the hinges on those hoods are part of our periodic maintenance. Also, she suggested that we not open or close those hoods unless our hands are clean and dry. Perhaps even cover the blade before we close the hood. We're not likely to change the design of the slicers. We're using the industry's best slicer. Given we're stuck with these slicers, I think we have a couple reasonable options now," said Dave.

"That's a good thing," said Milo. "And it helps me at my store. Now that I understand, I have something to manage. I have something I can look at other than simply retraining my team."

"Goes without saying. And thank you," said Dave. "We would not have learned anything from this event if it weren't for you questioning what had happened. We needed to dig deeper. That was my failure in not asking for that. I owe you a big thank you."

"Yeah. We should investigate all of our events, and the near misses, in this same way. If we learn the right lessons, we can prevent the next event from ever occurring," said Milo.

"You're right. This has been a huge lesson for me," said Dave. "We too often just excuse things as human error. Clearly, there's so much more we should learn behind what looks like a simple mistake."

"We're getting there," said Milo.

Dave could not see the grin on the other end of the phone, but Milo was feeling really good about his decision to push. It was bad that an artisan had to get 14 stitches. It would be tragic if no one learned from her event.

FLIGHT

Friday night. Date night. Well, a quiet evening at home with his wife. Kids put to bed. A movie, and some homemade popcorn. Not microwavable popcorn, nor heat over the fire Jiffy pop. Real popcorn, made in a little red popcorn cart Isabel had bought Milo when they moved into their new home. Heavily buttered, lightly salted – it was an indulgence for Milo.

Milo and Isabel alternated their movie picks. This week, it was Milo's turn and he'd chosen *Flight* with Denzel Washington, one of Milo's favorites actors. Denzel played a commercial airline pilot who piloted an aircraft that crashed into a field next to a rural Midwestern church. Milo figured with Denzel in the lead, it had to be a good action flick. For Isabel, it looked like a sleeper. Isabel wasn't keen on flying, and even less interested in watching movies about flying.

Both Milo and Isabel were surprised by the movie. The action took up very little of the movie; this was a decidedly human drama. Denzel plays Captain Whip Whitaker, a flamboyant pilot who is firmly convinced that he is the best pilot in the air. From his early childhood, with a Tuskegee airman father, Whip Whitaker knew he was going to be a pilot. And he was a good one.

He was also an alcoholic. And that was not where Milo wanted to see his favorite actor go. Milo was predisposed to like Captain Whitaker, to forgive his failings – which is probably why the studios cast Denzel in the part.

The movie began with a pretty unfavorable picture of Captain Whip and the picture only got worse as the movie progressed - adding interest for Isabel, creating discomfort for Milo. And then the crash occurred, a crash caused by a mechanical failure on the aircraft with Captain Whip at the controls. Not the more typical accident caused by "pilot error," this one was clearly a mechanical issue.

In the immediate aftermath of the accident, Captain Whip was considered a hero for having miraculously landed the plane with minimal loss of life. Until they discovered that Captain Whip had consumed alcohol before the flight and was likely intoxicated. He had even snuck a few of the little bottles from the galley when the flight attendants weren't looking. He had been drinking when the mechanical failure occurred. Despite his drinking, he crash-landed the aircraft like no other pilot could, at least as the story presented it.

What seemed to Milo an action movie had turned into a drama. And the drama was about what to do with Denzel's Captain Whitaker. The allegation of drinking was out in the open, yet disputed. Captain Whip would have to testify to a National Transportation Safety Board hearing. "Deny" his attorney repeated like a broken record. Just keep denying and the problem would go away. No one could prove he was drinking or drunk when the aircraft crashed, killing a few on board. No breathalyzer or toxicology tests had been run in the aftermath of the crash. And did it matter? The accident was clearly caused by the mechanical failure. The accident would have happened whether Captain Whip was intoxicated or not. Captain Whip's piloting kept people from dying. He was not the cause of death; he was instead a lifesaver - an intoxicated one, but a lifesaver nonetheless.

Isabel, who thought she might be reading a book or scanning her phone throughout the movie, was now watching intently. This was not about highly polished, perfect people; it was a movie opening a window to the screwed up nature of human beings. Milo could feel it happening. This was not going to be a brainless respite from his week at work. It was not going to be an escapist ride. It was instead a study of human behavior, and importantly, a study on human accountability. Should Denzel's character get away with flying intoxicated? Did Milo want his hero to come out unscathed? Did it matter that the intoxication was not the cause of the aircraft accident? Was the intoxication a wrong in itself?

"Crap," Isabel heard Milo say as he put a pillow over his face. "Crap, Crap, Crap."

"Are you alright?" Isabel asked, reaching over to Milo.

"Nooooo," Milo responded in a low extended voice.

"Why? What's the matter? I know you like Denzel Washington and all, but..."

"Because I have been here before, as a kid," said Milo.

"What do you mean?" asked Isabel.

"This is Uncle Julio. I've been here before. I've watched a few family fights, generally at a holiday meal with the entire family, back when I was in high school. My father would get into it with his sisters. Dad believed that Uncle Julio got what he deserved spending three years in jail. His sisters didn't agree. That time in jail changed Uncle Julio. He was never the same. He lived only about 3 years after he got out, but in those three years he was not the happy, fun-loving guy he was before he went to jail. He went to jail Uncle Julio and came out a confused, lonely ex-con. Holidays and family gatherings were awful while he was alive. Dad and his sisters invariably ended up screaming at each other about whether Uncle Julio got what he deserved. They saw Uncle Julio. My dad saw those kids on the school bus."

Isabel saw that Milo was crying. His voice slowed, as he tried his best to contain his emotions.

"I am so sorry, honey," said Isabel.

"I never really took sides in the argument," said Milo. "Heck, I just went to my bedroom or walked outside if we were at an auntie's house. I just wanted to get away from it – the screaming, just the emotion of it all. I liked Uncle Julio before he went to jail. I felt sorry for him when he came out. I didn't see much of him after his release. I was already off making my way as an adult. And today, as you know, we don't really have the big family gatherings. Uncle Julio's accident and its aftermath basically tore the family apart." Milo took a breath. "And that's probably the saddest part for our family. I just remember us all being so close when I was a kid. Now, we rarely get together and if we do, we have to follow the Alvarez Golden Rule: 'thou shalt not speak of Uncle Julio.'"

"I'm so sorry we watched this movie," said Isabel. "I had no idea it would bring up those memories."

"No, its ok. I'm the one who picked it. It was good to see the movie. It's finally given me some peace," said Milo.

"What do you mean?"

"I never really took sides in the Uncle Julio debate, in part because I think I tilted toward the side of my aunts. Uncle Julio didn't hurt anyone. It just seemed unfair to put him in jail if he caused no harm. And I really loved him. I missed him while he was in prison and my dad certainly wasn't going to allow me to go visit him. My dad shunned his brother after his DUI."

There was silence. Isabel could see that Milo's mind was somewhere, but not right there with her. They had paused the movie, just at the point where Captain Whip was about to testify before the National Transportation Safety Board hearing. Captain Whip's attorney had told him that if he remained silent and stuck to his story, he'd come out unscathed. All he had to do was lie about drinking on that flight.

The paused screen shot was of Captain Whip Whitaker just before he responded to the Board member's question. Milo looked at Captain Whip, memories of Uncle Julio swirling around in his head.

"Denzel's gotta do it. He has to come clean. And he has to go to jail," blurted Milo.

"You're right," said Isabel as she snuggled closer to Milo, laying her head in his shoulder. "What Denzel did was wrong. It doesn't matter that he didn't cause the accident or even that he probably saved a bunch of lives. He took a gamble with every life on that airplane. He deserves to be punished!"

Milo sat on the edge of his bed, ready to turn off the light after a very late date night with his wife. "We are responsible for what we can control," Milo thought to himself. "Once we've controlled what we can, life's a gamble. Whether we cause harm or not is not the issue. Accountability is about the risks we choose to take."

Milo crawled into bed and laid his head down to sleep. Reaching to turn out the light, Milo said to Isabel, "Hated it. But that was a great movie."

It had been swirling around his head for some time. What role did the outcome really play in accountability? Four months into his journey, Milo's obsession with societal and workplace accountability had not given him an answer. Everything Milo saw in the press very directly tied accountability to bad outcomes. The news was essentially a log of bad outcomes, with an ensuing dialogue about who to blame, and who to put in jail. Milo recognized the trend even in himself. He had been using the words, "no harm, no foul" throughout the last four months. He said it after Fred's skateboard accident. He said it after Fred's "wow" note. With his entire team, he'd been taking a "no harm, no foul" approach. And strangely, when there was harm – to Patti Foster – Dave's Subs had called "no foul." Something was not making sense but Milo kept digging.

Milo was not just questioning "no harm, no foul," but thoroughly rejecting it. Accountability should have very little to do with the actual outcome. Captain Whip Whitaker had chosen to fly a commercial airliner while under the influence of alcohol. For that he should go to jail, as should any other pilot caught doing the same – regardless of whether there was an incident or a heroic landing that actually saved people's lives. Uncle Julio had decided to drive, yet again, to the pub to get drunk, knowing very well he was going to attempt to drive himself home.

It simply did not matter that neither Captain Whip nor Uncle Julio wanted to cause harm. That was not the issue; it was their decision to risk the lives of others that was on the table. Milo was convinced. To be just, it had to be about the conduct, not the outcome. For Milo, that's exactly what recklessness was about. That conscious disregard of risk, that gamble a human makes when they choose to be reckless. It's that risk monitor pounding on the door of the System 2 brain, "This is a hazard. Don't do it!"

Milo could see it in his own life, his conscious brain attempting sometimes to rationalize away what the risk monitor was so accurately seeing. Perhaps it was his deeply ingrained pursuit of happiness. Something inside us that caused us to disregard the hazard we clearly saw. As a society we'd reconciled that the decision to *knowingly* cause harm came with public censure and criminal penalty. Child abuse. Theft. Murder. Arson. Milo had no problem with these in his growing model of workplace accountability. Nor, in his mind, did society have it wrong.

Recklessness was different. The person who acts recklessly has no intention to harm, only a recognition that they are gambling with others when they make the reckless choice. Uncle Julio, Captain Whip, they didn't set out to cause harm. Heck, Uncle Julio was a likeable drunk.

Milo had arrived at the belief that it was our job as a society to get the Uncle Julios and Whip Whitakers of the world back on the right track. It was society's job, an employer's job, a father's job, to create artificial danger as a very real consequence for reckless choices. Make the choice to gamble with the lives or safety of others, and you will go to jail. Milo could love Uncle Julio – and he did. He could appreciate the skill Captain Whip demonstrated in landing that airplane with minimal casualties – and he did. But both Uncle Julio and Captain Whip deserved their prison sentences. Of that, Milo was now convinced and at peace.

THE GULF

Milo was left drained by the movie *Flight*. For the first time, he felt like telling Dave to assign this workplace accountability task to someone else. For Milo, around nearly every corner he turned in life, there stood the topic of accountability. Kids and grades – accountability. Drivers doing weird things – accountability. Evening news – accountability. Employees – accountability. It was everywhere, and Milo was feeling exhausted.

Milo was not the kind of guy, though, who would let a problem go unfixed, or leave a question unanswered. Milo had identified the mistakes at one end of the spectrum, those things we humans never intend to do. At the other end of the spectrum were those much more intentional things like truly wanting to cause harm. In the middle was reckless, the gamble with another's life. And Milo had finally resolved a question left unanswered for him for more than 15 years, that being the role of the actual outcome of a risky human choice. Captain Whip and Uncle Julio answered that question for him.

Yet, Milo knew that there remained an incredibly large subset of human behavior still unlabeled. In fact, for Milo, the majority of the behavior he saw around him did not fall under either the human error or reckless label. Like Lucy, Milo knew he needed to come up with that label before he had any hope of fixing it. He needed to keep thinking and observing.

A few weeks later on his drive to work, he got his label.

In every town, there are three types of roads. The neighborhood roads where speed limits are very low, the highways where speed limits are at their maximum, and the roads between neighborhoods, maintained by cities and townships, where speeds are in between. Those middle roads generally have marked lanes, two on each side of a center median used for turns. These are more heavily travelled than the neighborhood roads, and have many more starts and stops than on the highways.

It was on one of these roads where he saw it. Milo was driving perhaps 40 mph in the inside lane, when a young woman pulled up beside him. Actually, she was passing him. The speed limit was 45, so she probably was not speeding. But that was not the issue for Milo. It was the fact that she was eating a bowl of cereal as she drove. One hand on the wheel at most, sometimes both on the cereal, one on the bowl, one on the spoon, she was apparently steering with her legs. Seeing her eating a bowl of cereal was not overly surprising for Milo, as he'd seen people do a lot of crazy things while driving - texting, reading a book, applying makeup, drinking coffee or smoking a cigarette. The cereal was just unique. So unique, that it pushed him over the top.

They came to a gentle stop at the next intersection. He rolled down his passenger side window.

"Hey, you, lady, miss, roll down your window," he yelled as his hands motioned feebly in a "roll the window down" pantomime.

She cheerfully complied. "What's up? Tail light out?" she responded, as if she thought Milo was hitting on her.

"That bowl of cereal you're eating," he said.

"Want some?" she responded quickly.

"Don't you think eating cereal while driving is a tad bit dangerous?" asked Milo.

"What?"

"The cereal bowl. Don't you think it's dangerous?" Milo repeated, raising his voice at the possibility she didn't hear the first time.

The young lady in the car didn't say another word. She simply raised one finger as a sign to Milo that he'd crossed a line with her, rolled up her window, and went on her way when the light changed, still eating her cereal.

Milo thought about that encounter the rest of the day at work. That had definitely not been a typical encounter for Milo. He wasn't sure what had possessed him to confront a stranger over driving while eating cereal. "It probably wasn't even against the law," he thought to himself.

Throughout the day, though, no matter how hard he tried, he could not put that young woman in the reckless bucket. He was convinced, in the very short time he had with her, that she actually thought eating the bowl of cereal while driving her car was a reasonable thing to do. It was not human error; she wasn't inadvertently eating a bowl of cereal on her way to work. And it was not reckless. Milo was convinced her risk monitor was not firing.

Instead, this behavior was right there in between, within that gulf of human behavior that he'd seen in every human being. For most of us, Milo believed, there was a very large gulf in which most of our daily aberrant human behavior occurred. This young lady was just focused on getting to work. That was her mission in the moment. Perhaps she'd woken up a little late and didn't have time to eat before she left for work. Add to that the fact that cereal bowls are so portable. She could have gone through drive thru at a local fast food restaurant and eaten a muffin/egg combo on the way to work, but why bother? Sixty seconds of effort in her kitchen, and she had that bowl of cereal ready to go. It was everyday life for this young lady, in spite of the fact that Milo found it astonishing enough to confront her at a stoplight.

It raised a few troublesome questions for Milo. Why did he see the risk but the young woman did not? It hit Milo that this was one of those "in the eye of the beholder" kind of problem. He saw the cereal driving as risky, whereas the young lady did not. Who was right? Who got to be the judge? Was it society that established what was acceptable or not? Drinking a cup of coffee on the way to work was acceptable; eating a bowl of cereal was not?

As a manager, Milo knew it was in his job description to decide what was acceptable and unacceptable behavior on the part of his artisans. And it was up to Dave to decide what was acceptable at Dave's Subs as a whole, and what was acceptable from his managers. That was simply part of the deal of working at Dave's Subs.

At a societal level, deciding acceptable and unacceptable was probably left to the legislature and the courts, or even just the norms of social behavior that defined what was acceptable and what was not. And in each case, it seemed a trade. Drinking a cup of coffee on the way to work surely imposed some level of hazard, yet we've chosen for now to socially endorse it. "It might be against the law, not sure if it is," Milo thought, "but it surely is not something a police officer is going to pull me over for."

When the risk outweighed the reward - in the eyes of the beholder - it was seen as unjustifiably risky. It was at-risk as a choice. And that was the label Milo finally landed on, "at-risk behavior." Eating cereal on the way to work was at-risk behavior for Milo, but apparently something reasonable for the young lady eating the cereal.

The difference of opinion, it seemed to Milo, was the natural course of things. Our risk monitors all work differently; we are alerted to different risks. If Milo wanted to change the behavior of the young lady eating the cereal, he would just have to sit down and convince her that eating cereal while driving was dangerous to other drivers, and to her.

Milo's thoughts drifted to what had been a hot topic when he was an artisan at the original Dave's Subs store - plastic gloves.

The shop was open only 25 hours a week. 10-3, Monday through Friday. In those hours Milo and his team would produce 2000 subs. Speed, throughput – it was essential to the profitability of the store. Some restaurants would stay open 24 hours. If they have paid for the space, why not take advantage of it? Yet, keeping open meant labor costs, and in the middle of the night, could a trickle of customers purchase enough food to support the added costs of keeping the store open?

Dave set up his shop at the other end of the 24/7 spectrum. He located his sub shops in high-rise office buildings knowing that his customers would come only during lunchtime. Thankfully, people needed to eat. And downtown office workers had a tendency to eat out – their lifestyle often not supporting waking early to prepare a brown bag lunch.

High quality ingredients. Fast and friendly service. And when he said fast, he meant fast. Dave and each of his managers continually looked for ways to improve throughput. Don't offer fountain drinks, only cans and plastic bottles. Don't offer toasted rolls. Take no cash. Paper receipts.

Of course, it had not always been so refined. Six stores in six years meant lots of opportunity to refine the system.

In many fast food restaurants where employees have to assemble the food, they use a unique set of clear plastic gloves for each customer. After making the food, the employee removes his gloves and then tenders the cash from the customer. That's where the problem lay. Touching the cash register, touching money. Money, while valuable, was not clean, by any stretch of one's imagination. No one literally launders money, putting it in the washing machine and deciding between the hot or cold water cycle. So, like very other sub shop, Dave had initially adopted the industry standard, one set of plastic gloves per customer.

And that was exactly how Milo was trained, one pair of gloves per customer. Yet, Dave found that his employees had a tendency to drift away from that behavior, even more so than at other fast food restaurants. Dave regularly spoke to his employees, including Milo, about the importance of changing gloves. It worked, sort of. Depending.

Dave's employees knew that they worked at a special place. Well, a unique place. Nobody touched cash at Dave's; this was the system Dave had designed to achieve the fast in "fast and friendly." In fact, there weren't even any cash registers. Customers swiped their own cards, and as long as the bill was under $25 dollars, they were not even required to sign the receipt. Artisans asked their customers to grab the receipt as it spun out of the countertop printer.

Given how Milo and his fellow artisans understood the risk, there was no real reason to change gloves. Just keep touching food, and nothing else, and there didn't seem to be a rational reason to change gloves.

Yet, Dave had a policy. Change gloves between customers. His artisans were expected to follow the policy. It was that simple for Dave. And when Dave was around watching, that's exactly what happened. Yet, when Dave was out of sight, the glove changing stopped.

So how did Dave know? Dave ordered gloves based upon serving 2000 customers each week at his original location. That meant a little more than 2000 pairs of plastic gloves each week. Yet, there came a time during Milo's days at the original store where Dave found himself ordering fewer and fewer gloves. Initially it started as way too many in the back storage room, and then it led to Dave ordering less in his weekly supply order. It didn't hit him at first. Dave would order 2100 each week, then it was 1800, then 1500. When it crossed that 1500 glove threshold, it occurred to Dave that something was wrong. His risk monitor fired.

Milo was one of seven artisans at the original store. With five workstations, it was a little larger than Milo's store #6. Milo remembers the meeting with Dave and his fellow artisans, one of those pre-shift meetings with everyone sitting around a few tables at the front of the store, only half-awake and half-listening.

"So, guys, what's the deal with the gloves?" Dave began.

"What do you mean?" responded one of Milo's fellow artisans.

"I ordered only 1500 plastic gloves this week," said Dave.

"Is that a good thing, or a bad thing?" asked another artisan in a quizzical tone, tinged slightly with sarcasm.

"It's a bad thing when we serve 2000 customers in a week." responded Dave. "I watch you guys remove gloves between customers. Yet, it's clear we're using fewer gloves than we have customers."

"It's about speed, Dave," responded Chris, one of the higher performing artisans in the group. "You want 3000 subs per week at this location; we don't always have time to remove gloves between customers."

Dave sat there, somewhat dejected, not saying a word, perhaps formulating a response.

"Before you say it," said that same high performing artisan looking directly at Dave, "know that we're not like other fast food chains. We don't have to touch the money."

"But, Chris, it's our rule," snapped Dave, apparently a bit taken aback by Chris's remarks.

"Yeah, but speed is king," said Chris.

Milo remembered that staff meeting like it were yesterday. He'd never been around someone as brash as Chris. If it were not for a few other artisans, including Milo himself, coming to Chris's defense, affirming his perspective, Milo believed that might have been Chris's last day at Dave's Subs. Chris was admitting to deviating from a procedural rule. And he was boldly admitting it to Dave, essentially saying that a safety rule was taking a back seat to speed, to profitability.

Looking back, Milo now had a frame of reference. It was not human error. It was not reckless. Milo himself was one of those who would occasionally break the rule. Busy lunch rush, Dave not standing behind him, he'd sometimes break the rule. Did his risk monitor go off? "No," Milo knew. The artisans had an unwritten rule. If the store needed to pick up the pace, drop the changing of gloves. Did it save much time? Perhaps 15 seconds, but that was enough for Milo and his fellow artisans who were focused on speed and production. If they had to touch the money, they would always wash their hands and change gloves. If they could make the sandwich and not touch anything other than the food, they made the choice not to change gloves.

Somewhere between the human error, and the reckless act was another zone. It was a choice to not change gloves. It was not human error. Nor, however, did Milo's risk monitor go off each time he failed to change gloves. Milo and his fellow artisans could keep the same gloves between customers and feel like they were in a "safe" place. And in hindsight, it seemed the artisans' risk monitors were firing accurately; they were in a safe place, if Dave's decision to abandon the plastic gloves was any vindication.

This wasn't very different, Milo thought, than the young lady eating the cereal while driving. For Milo, it clearly looked risky; for the young woman, it just seemed efficient. It was not human error, nor was it a reckless choice to knowingly gamble. No, this was subtler. It was that middle ground between human error and a reckless choice; Milo now had the label for that middle ground. At-risk.

At-risk was the shorthand label to describe what was happening in that space between human error and reckless conduct. At-risk behavior was a choice, a choice that came with risk. Whether it was a deviation from a rule was not, in Milo's mind, the operative factor. Dave wrote the glove rule to avoid a known hazard. Dave saw not wearing gloves as his team taking a risk with his customers. It was for Dave, an at-risk behavior, an at-risk choice. Just as Milo thought the young woman eating cereal was engaged in an at-risk activity.

So he had the label: at-risk behavior. Now what? Milo was still struggling with which part of his brain made the choice. Chris, in telling Dave why his artisans chose not to change gloves between customers, was clearly thinking with his System 2 brain. He'd done a cost/benefit analysis, no matter how deep, and the clear speed benefit outweighed the minimal safety cost. Chris, Milo, and the other artisans knew they were deviating from the rule when they chose not to change gloves. Yet, none of them felt they were putting customers in harm's way. Touch money, risk monitor fires, artisans change gloves. No money exchange, touching only food, utensils, and the counter – no alarms, no need to change gloves.

A human mistake was a human mistake. Everyone could see it through the same set of eyes. The same was true with recklessness. The reckless person, by definition, sees the unjustifiable risk they take, as do those looking in from the outside. Milo knew that at-risk behaviors were different. The outside observer would see it as risky, yet they would believe that the person engaged in the choice was not seeing the risk. At-risk behaviors had that unique "in the eye of the beholder" effect going on.

Milo could look into his own team now and see a number of at-risk behaviors. The most obvious was that gluten-free bread check. He'd sometimes find his team making the choice not to do the check. The store got busy and an artisan let the safety check slide. Milo knew that his team was not choosing to put their customers in harm's way. They simply believed, looking at the bread themselves, that they could complete the confirmation on their own. No reason to yell out "I've got gluten-free," when they could see the crosshatch pattern right there in their hand.

But it went deeper than merely making the call for others to respond. It was also a reminder to the sub artisans themselves to even do the check. For the regulars at the store, it was a familiar sign. For those regular customers who wanted a gluten-free roll, it was an auditory signal that the store, and its sub artisan, was taking it seriously. Along with the new coasters now being passed to customers ordering gluten-free rolls, it was another opportunity for the customer to participate in the safety check.

When Milo saw at-risk behavior among his staff, he now was better equipped to talk to them. "Here is the hazard we are trying to control," Milo would say. "If we skip the check, we put our business or our customer at risk."

Milo was making sense of it. Yet, one thing still bothered him. Was this newfound behavior really a choice? Milo would drive with friends that he was sure never used a turn signal. And he went out to dinner with buddies he was sure never washed their hands after going to the restroom.

Both seemed risky to Milo. Yet, both looked more like simple habits than choice. Habits, Milo knew, resided more in the System 1 brain than in System 2. Once a behavior is learned, or becomes habit, the subconscious System 1 brain simply takes over.

Driving was a good example of that. New and novel decisions required System 2 thinking; System 1 took control when the task was routine, habitual, seeming to require little or no conscious thinking. Then it hit him. Both System 1 and System 2 could make what we commonly refer to as choices. Some choices are conscious, some or most appear more subconscious. Habit appeared as a subconscious choice, a learned behavior, so that the System 2 brain could get on with more creative, interesting thinking.

The risk monitor was a different matter though. The risk monitor, for practical purposes, alerted the System 2 brain to hazards. "Hello, Hello… are you going to step in here?" it might yell to our conscious brain, particularly when the risk was grave. Whether System 1 or System 2 made the choice of how to respond to the perceived risk was irrelevant to the operation of the risk monitor. It didn't care what part of the brain was making a bad choice; it was out to alert System 2 of the hazard so that it would quickly discontinue whatever risky choice was being made.

Now Milo was a smart guy. He knew he was not in control of his subconscious choices. His life choices may have trained his subconscious to make the choices it made, but in real time he, thinking with his System 2 brain, had no real operational control.

Given that, he truthfully had no proof that the risk monitor was independently alerting his System 1 brain. But Milo had a strong inclination it was. Milo could sort of see it in operation. Get a little close to the edge of a train platform, and he'd instinctively move back. Was his risk monitor talking to his System 1 brain, "No reason to alert System 2, we'll take care of this?" It appeared that the step back just happened. Milo could watch his mother instinctively move a glass away from the edge of a table when his girls were visiting. She'd do it while having an animated conversation about the latest civil rights issue in the news, not even realizing she'd moved the glass. Her risk monitor would pick it up, and her System 1 brain would apparently react. Was her risk monitor doing the same, "No reason to alert System 2, we'll take care of this?" That question Milo felt he could leave to research psychologists and economists like Kahneman. His brain was already pushed far beyond his level of comfort.

What did make sense is that there was a class of behavior, or choice, between human error and reckless that represented all of those things we somehow choose to do, but don't consciously see or appreciate the risk in doing. For now, he'd call them at-risk behaviors.

Treble Means Triple

Fall was in the air, which meant Milo needed to get out onto the course one last time with John before the leaves dropped and the snow began to fall. There were two things Milo and John did when they went golfing – they golfed, or at least tried to, and they talked. And Milo had plenty to talk about since their last outing.

"So, I have been thinking about that word you used on me the last time we went golfing," said Milo.

"What was that? From what I can remember, you were playing a lot better than me. Heck, I was probably calling you a lot of things," said John.

"Reckless," said Milo.

"Oh, that skateboarding thing," said John.

"Yeah, that's the word. Reckless. And I think you were right. I was being reckless watching my team play with a skateboard in the store," said Milo.

"Sorry, man, didn't mean to throw you under the bus," said John.

"No, that's ok. I learned a lot under there," replied Milo.

Today was a better golfing day for both John and Milo, notwithstanding the shorter executive course.

"You know, next time, we should think about playing the big course," said John. "You know, with holes longer than 300 yards. We just might graduate from this short course."

"Hmmm…we'll see at the end of today's round," Milo said, preoccupied. "John, you gotta know that you sent me on quite the journey with that word."

"What's that?"

"Well, first to understand what the word even meant. Then to understand why we humans stick labels like that on each other," said Milo.

"Yeah, I was kinda rough, huh? Maybe it's just fun. As I can remember, I felt good doing it. Seemed to help mitigate the pain I was feeling from my game," said John.

"Seriously, it really got me thinking," said Milo. "You know we screwed up a sandwich for a lady who needed a gluten-free roll?" said Milo.

"Dude, I think everyone in New Jersey knew you did that. I think about it every time I see those billboards for that law firm, Dewey, Cheatum and Howe."

"It's Lawrence, Foster, and…something…I forget. But the truth is we did screw up. We deserved to make it right with that customer. And I agreed with the attorney that no amount of money could really make up for missing her only child's wedding," Milo paused, thoughtfully. "What's interesting to me is that we labeled our screw–up a mistake, a *human error*. It was clear our employee didn't mean Patti Foster any harm. She did nothing reckless – and yet, we paid. And that's the point. The label we used internally was 'human error' and it had meaning. We messed up. I guess that's the American system of justice – he who makes a mistake pays for the mistake. There was no recklessness, just a mistake. As a business, we rightfully paid out a claim, to cover that customer's very real losses."

"Ok, seems reasonable. So tie this back to our last golf outing. You're losing me a bit," said John.

"No one was fired. Not me, not my employee, Alisha. And the business was not closed down. We made a mistake. As a business, we paid a price, but we moved on," said Milo. "My point here is that the labels I've been coming up with – with assistance from some of my dearest friends like you - have meaning. If someone had been reckless, someone likely would have been fired. Recklessness is different than a simple mistake."

"Ok, seems reasonable. So, again, before I whack you with this putter, tie this back to our last golf outing," said John.

"You got me thinking about recklessness. And why we link punishment, or discipline, to reckless choices. If you label me reckless, sanction seems to follow. And with it came, if I can remember, a bit of condemnation," said Milo.

"You bet it did. You were gambling with your store by letting that big guy skateboard in the shop," said John.

"You're right! I was weighing the pros and cons, watching it happen, and even though I recognized there was at least some chance this was a bad idea, I just sat there and allowed it to happen. Which brings me to sanction. It got me to thinking about the role of sanction. What's the point of sanction, anyway?" asked Milo.

"I suspect you're gonna tell me," said John.

"As you Canadians say, 'You 'betcha,'" replied Milo. "It just so happens that I've got the perfect example to illustrate the answer."

"Remember back when you had trouble with that landlord, when you were moving out of your old apartment?" asked Milo.

"Yeah, you helped me quite a bit with that!" said John.

"I just happened to know about treble damages," said Milo. "Your landlord was well beyond reckless. He was just choosing to withhold your deposit under some claim that the walls were soiled beyond normal wear and tear. You knew it was bogus. Yet, you thought you'd spend on an attorney more than you would recover on the claim. That is, until I told you about treble damages, that you could receive three times what the landlord owed."

"Just that simple threat caused me to get my deposit back. Thank you for that," said John.

"Those treble damages were artificial consequences. There was no reason for the landlord to pay back your deposit. He was thinking you would simply walk away. But as soon as he knew that you were aware of the treble damages, he ponied up. The State of New Jersey helped you out. It created artificial danger. Mess unreasonably with Tenant John and you will pay triple what is owed. And that's artificial danger," said Milo.

"Yeah, so how does that help you?" asked John.

"As a manager, I need to think about where I use artificial danger. Recklessness is one of those cases. If you're willing to gamble, it will come with a price," said Milo. "You helped me figure that out."

"Do you talk about this stuff with anyone else?" asked John.

"A few… Dave, the owner, Isabel, my girls…" Milo grinned.

"You are becoming one sick dude," said John.

Milo was fixated on the idea of artificial danger. Maybe it was because of all of the advice that Dave and he had received after the Patti Foster event. "Fire her," being the consistent theme. Yet, none of them could really explain how that solved anything. It surely didn't get Patti Foster to her daughter's wedding. It was a knee jerk reaction to harm. Someone had been harmed, someone needed to pay a price, as if that fixed anything.

And then there was the "natural consequences" crowd who said to forget sanction, let us just experience the natural consequences of our behavior. That, to Milo, was just as pointless and irrational. Let the pilot experience the natural consequences of a decision to deviate from a safety protocol? Only at the risk of a plane full of dead plane passengers.

Milo looked at where we created artificial consequences, in the workplace and in life. He spent most of his time thinking of the latter, identifying a noticeable trend. Artificial consequences seemed most tied to the protection of others, like for the pilot flying the airplane. Society spent significantly less time writing rules and associated consequences to keep people from hurting themselves. Sure there was that flap about preventing New Yorkers from ordering jumbo sodas, but those were the exception to the rule. Prohibition and tobacco bans haven't worked either. Society's rules were mostly about keeping humans from harming other humans. Even the drunk driving law that got Uncle Julio thrown in jail for three years was more about protecting the public, other drivers, and those children on the bus, than it was about protecting Uncle Julio.

Perhaps our genetic predisposition to self-preservation inclined us to more readily recognize risks to ourselves than to others, Milo surmised. After all, there was no rule against putting your own hand in the fire. Yet, forcibly shove another person's hand in the fire, and we have undoubtedly broken a social rule.

Self-preservation. Self-centeredness. The reality, Milo knew, was that individuals think individually, and mostly about themselves. That's where Uncle Julio was when he drank and drove. He knew he was having a good time at the pub, and he thought the risk of hurting someone was low. Likewise, Milo's six-year-old daughter would be thinking of herself when she snuck that bag of potato chips up to her bedroom. Milo knew he could try to convince his daughter of the threat of ants, but until she'd actually seen it, and possibly until she'd actually been stung by one, it looked more like an old wives' tale than practical reality. Yet, the threat of discipline (and possibly of disappointing Daddy) for getting caught was enough to keep his daughter from continuing the behavior.

Milo knew his thinking was getting pretty basic. "How could humanity even exist without a set of self-imposed artificial danger driving its actions?" Milo wondered. As Milo was discovering, the need for artificial danger or consequences seemed to be everywhere.

For Milo, John's landlord's refusal to return a security deposit was an excellent example of the need for artificial danger. The natural consequence of the landlord wrongly keeping the deposit was that the landlord kept the deposit. Back in the day, John might have challenged the landlord to a duel. Death of one of them would perhaps have been the natural consequences of one party refusing to return that which did not belong to him.

Thankfully, Milo thought, we've moved beyond those days. Instead, we live in an advanced society filled with artificial danger. Don't return a deposit, and face the threat of paying triple what you owe. No matter how much we've evolved as humans, it seems, we still require society's threat of artificial danger to help keep us, as a species, honest.

Thinking of the threat of disciplinary sanction as artificial danger helped Milo make sense of it all. Milo needed to know when disciplinary sanction would work. And why it would work. It astonished Milo how many people were willing to pull out that club, metaphorically, and whack another person without knowing why they were whacking in the first place, or what they hoped to achieve with the whack.

Was it just those people sitting back in their recliners watching the 6:00 news, eager to see another person getting what the recliner folks thought they deserved? Milo was now troubled by that notion of getting what one deserved. What exactly was it we all deserved?

Aye, Aye Coach

Fall meant football. Professional football, college football, and high school football. Milo has always been a big sports fan, although he'd played little himself. Most of Milo's evening guitar students were not athletes, at least at the level of the varsity team. Playing an instrument at a high level meant practice. It was the rare high-school student who could commit to a sport while also studying music.

Milo had one student, though, who excelled at both. His name was Randall Jenkins. Randall had committed to keep his guitar going while also playing on the varsity football team. Tall and wiry, Randall played wide receiver. Those fingers so well trained on the guitar were great for feeling the football right into his hands. Get the ball near him and he'd catch it.

Randall knew Milo loved football. He'd spoken to his football coach about Milo and asked if Milo could join the team on the sideline one Friday night. It was a gesture to his teacher, to give something back. "I think you'll like my coach," said Randall. "He's always telling me what to do, like you."

It was a great night. Just fifty feet closer than a standard seat in the stands, yet the view was entirely different. Milo's senses were overwhelmed. Things were brighter, louder, more hurried. Milo stood just five feet away from Randall's coach. The coach talked on the headset to his assistants up in the booth. He relayed plays through players coming in and out of the game. Randall's team, obviously, was not perfect on the field. Footballs were fumbled, catches were missed. It was a close game, but Randall's team won. To Milo's surprise, however, there was little yelling from the coach. He was extremely positive with his players, giving them high-fives when they left the field. Rarely anything corrective, or negative. He seemed more cheerleader than coach.

Milo didn't get the chance to catch up with Randall after the game. Randall had his post game huddle, then straight to the showers and off with friends after the game. Milo did get the chance to catch up at their next lesson, that next Tuesday evening.

"Randall, thank you for the invitation to the game," said Milo.

"Hope you enjoyed it," said Randall.

"I do have one question," said Milo. "You said your coach is always telling you what to do."

"Yeah, he is," replied Randall. "He's always coaching me. If he sees me make a bad decision, he's on it. He's always coaching me."

"But I didn't see him coach you, or anyone during that entire game," said Milo.

"Oh, no, during the game he's calling the plays," said Randall. "It's at practice that he coaches me."

"Say that again," said Milo, feeling like he was missing something.

"Coach Burleson says that he coaches us hard during practice, so that we can all go enjoy the game," said Randall. "Come over to the school at 2:30 any and every day of the week. You'll see what I mean."

Milo did just that. Practice was totally unlike the game. Game noise was replaced by coach noise. Coach Burleson spent the entire time yelling at the kids on the field. Milo couldn't tell if he yelled so that they could hear him through their helmets, or if he just yelled for emphasis. Milo got a chance to watch a scrimmage, where the first string offense played the second string defense, and visa versa. Lots of errors: missed catches, missed tackles, fumbles. Coach Burleson would just grimace, shake his head, and on one occasion, tossed his clipboard.

Real games and scrimmages were riddled with mistakes. That's sports. That's being human. Milo started to notice a pattern when Coach Burleson yelled. The coach yelled instruction. It might be to move to a different location of the field. It might be to look in a different direction. Each instruction involved an affirmative instruction that his players could respond to.

Coach Burleson didn't yell when the running back fumbled the ball or when a linebacker missed an obvious tackle. Milo might not have seen it before his newfound journey, but it was clear as day to him now. Coach Burleson was letting the mistakes go. He was focusing on the choices his players were making. Every yell took the form of "hey, do this instead." And his players complied. He was letting go of the errors. He was "coaching" the players when they needed coaching. And, on one play during the scrimmage where a minor scuffle broke out between two players, the players were benched. Milo later saw them both running sprints along the far edge of the field, closely watched by one of the assistant coaches.

There it was. Milo could see the model at work in Coach Burleson. He was living with the mistakes – as if they didn't matter. Simply grieve the errors but move on – as quickly as possible – to those things that could be controlled. A sigh, a grimace, perhaps, and then move on. He wasn't coaching his players not to make mistakes. He was simply living with them.

The at-risk behaviors were different. Coach Burleson would yell at his players if they didn't have a piece of information they needed, or if they needed to make a different choice. "Back up another 5 yards," he'd yell at a cornerback. "Watch the split end," he'd yell at one of his linebackers.

And, when he'd seen something that crossed his line, he'd punish. Running laps if the players were lucky, running sprints if they were not.

Live with the error, coach the at-risk behavior, punish the reckless. That's what Milo was seeing in Coach Burleson. It was making Milo feel pretty good about the last six months. Not good for the consequences to Patti Foster, certainly, but good in the sense of that event's silver lining – what he had learned from the journey that that event had launched them all on. Milo was learning to be a better manager and, he thought, a better husband and father.

EDUCATING DAVE

Dave asked Milo to report on what he had been learning over the last several months. It was Milo's journey; Dave had set it in motion with his letter in response to the Patti Foster event, but he had given the heavy lifting to Milo. Milo had spent six months preparing for this discussion. He had played with the ideas of workplace justice more than most managers. In the course of his investigation, he had developed a philosophy. And now it was time to put it out, for Dave, and ultimately others, to critique.

So they met at Milo's store, on a Monday afternoon, after things had quieted down.

"So, here we sit. Roughly six months after Alisha's event," said Dave. "Are you ready?"

"Sure," said Milo. "I'm as ready as I'm ever going to be."

"Ok. Let's go."

"I'll start with this," said Milo. "You were right to write the letter. We human beings have an inescapable fallibility. And that fallibility sometimes shows itself in a spectacular way, such as the Patti Foster event. In that event, Patti, the press, our colleagues, weren't really judging Alisha; they were all judging the outcome. They saw a bad outcome, and they were looking for someone to blame. It's deeply embedded in our culture and probably human nature. Anyway, the letter was on target. There was no reason to fire Alisha for making a mistake," said Milo.

"Well, I'm thankful for that," said Dave. "But I'm hoping you learned more than just that after six months."

"I did," said Milo. "If our first curse for being human is our inescapable fallibility, we are cursed a second time."

"With?"

"Free will," said Milo.

"I thought that was a blessing?"

"Yeah, it depends on the context. It is a blessing, until that free will starts making unnecessarily risky choices. Then it appears to be a curse," said Milo. "And it's this free will that is the more important actor in the story. We're inescapably fallible in that we do things we never intend to do. We make mistakes. Human errors. We have some control over their rate, but we'll never eliminate them. We're just sorta stuck with that aspect of our being.

"The free will piece is different," continued Milo. "It's about how we make choices in life. Choices that sometimes result in increasing the likelihood of error, or choices that prevent me from mitigating the errors that I've already made."

"Give me an example," Dave was quick to interject.

"Not washing hands after touching money. Before gloves, we used to tell food workers to wash their hands if they touched money. Sometimes, they forgot. We had to live with that. It's the choice to not wash hands that's the problem, though, not the forgetting. I might forget once or twice out of 100 times. Yet, if I drift into a bad habit, it could be I never wash my hands after touching cash. Or, consider the choice, in a rush, to not bother checking to see if the back door is securely locked when closing the shop for the day. We convince ourselves that the risk is low, so we blow by the required check," said Milo.

"So what do you suggest we do with these behaviors?" said Dave.

"Well, after a lot of reading, and after exercising a *lot* of brain cells, I've come to call them at-risk behaviors. And I think we coach our employees when we see them. In an ideal world, we'd see artisans comfortable with coaching – politely – one another. The management books I've read call this peer-to-peer coaching. When I say coaching, I'm not talking about the first step of progressive discipline, another B-school term I've encountered. I'm talking about having a conversation with a fellow human being about a risk I see them taking, where they do not seem to see the risk themselves," said Milo.

"What about something like theft?" asked Dave. "Would you have us coach the thief? After all, stealing is a choice."

"Right, I think an employee who steals clearly opens themselves up to discipline. Theft is different from the at-risk behaviors I'm describing," said Milo.

Milo could see he was getting in the weeds; he needed to backtrack a bit. It was time to introduce Dave to the idea of the risk monitor.

"I read a book, *Thinking, Fast and Slow* by a Princeton professor named Daniel Kahneman. A friend of mine recommended it to me. Anyway, Kahneman and his colleague won the Nobel Prize in economics for their work in a new field of study called behavioral economics. Kahneman believes we have two brains, sort of. He calls them System 1 and System 2. They represent, in simple terms, our subconscious and our conscious minds.

"System 2 is the brain that you typically think of and value as your "brain." It's your thinking brain. System 1 is the brain that does all of the hard work, though. It's the brain that drives you to work, while your System 2 brain is churning away trying to figure out why the Jets lost again last night. With me so far?"

"Yep, my System 2 brain is keeping right there with you," said Dave.

"Great. I'm glad you have it. Now, I'm going to suggest we treat System 1 and System 2 decisions a bit differently when we're thinking about workplace accountability. Of course, Kahneman's brilliant – he won the Nobel Prize, after all. But there seemed to be a missing piece for me. So I made one up."

Dave raised an eyebrow.

"Kahneman might like it or he might not, but that's not my concern. It works for me. The missing piece was finding the hidden app that's always running in our brains. I call it the risk monitor, there since our days on the savannah trying to outwit all the things that were trying to eat us. Those of us without a well functioning app, or who were missing the latest update, lions or packs of hyenas quickly snapped up for dinner.

"The risk monitor is that part of our brain that keeps an eye out for hazards. Our System 2 brain can be searching for a cure for cancer, while our System 1 brain is brushing our teeth. The risk monitor just quietly hums along in the background, until it spots a hazard – say, the odd taste of your toothpaste as you notice only the hair gel out on the counter," said Dave.

"Yeah, I've made that mistake before," Dave said, thinking of the time in college he inadvertently used hair gel to brush his teeth.

"Our risk monitor is that application that's always running, alerting our conscious System 2 brain to threats. Now, with free will, we can always ignore the threat. The guy who steals from his employer? Short of being a sociopath, his risk monitor is surely alerting him to the wrongness of his conduct. In pursuit of what he wants, though, he ignores the input.

Back in the day, an artisan who didn't change gloves between customers most likely didn't have that risk monitor alerting, though. On this, I can actually speak from experience," Milo looked sheepishly at Dave.

"We go tooling along in our day, in a routine pumping out subs, keeping an eye on the artisan next to us to see how fast she was pumping them out. For a reasonably good artisan, after a few weeks on the job, his System 1 brain took on most of the work for us, freeing us up to be the other thing you ask – friendly! But that System 1 brain gets easily fooled," said Milo.

"So how do we deal with each type?" asked Dave.

"Like I said, we coach when we believe the behavior is at-risk. We coach when we believe our employee did not see the risk, that is, their risk monitor did not alert, or if it did, the conscious brain did not see it as an unjustifiable risk under the circumstances. But if the System 2 brain recognizes it as a risk, and chooses the behavior regardless, that's when we consider disciplinary action. The term for that behavior is reckless."

"Ok, I get it. But you know it begs the question: Who decides?" asked Dave.

"Great question. It's not the employee himself. It's those tasked to evaluate – managers, supervisors, owners sometimes. They have to put themselves in the shoes of the employee they're evaluating. They have to ask if they would have seen the risk if they had been standing in their shoes," responded Milo.

"Damn, dude. You're turning into a full-on human resources guy. Ever consider going to law school?" asked Dave. "My mom would sure be willing to write you a recommendation if you went over some of this stuff with her."

"Nah! I'm too happy at Dave's Subs," grinned Milo.

"I really do find this stuff intriguing, though. Let's get back to my story. It's hands down, one of the most important things I've learned these past six months and I need to make sure you get it," Milo paused to get Dave's attention. "It's critical that we do all this evaluating independently of the outcome," said Milo.

"What?" asked Dave. "You're gonna have to take me through that. I thought we were talking about events - which by definition have a bad outcome - that's what makes them events."

"I know. But this is the most important part of this. Let's say I cut a corner, not physically checking the back door is locked. It's become a habit; heck I never check now. Yet, one day the bread guy does not fully close the door. It looks closed, but it's not fully latched. And that evening, someone enters the open door and steals some of our equipment. Now, for what do you hold me accountable? Is the problem I forgot to check on the day the thief came by, or is the problem that I have drifted into not doing the check at all?" said Milo.

"Ok, I see. I think. It's the not checking that's the problem, not the forgetting to close the back door," said Dave.

"Right! The rest is luck, "fortuity" to use a legal word. That's why I say that we console the human error, we coach the at-risk, and we consider discipline for the reckless, and we do this all independent of the actual harm. It's the hazards we create that we're accountable for. Luck has no place in a system of justice, workplace or not," said Milo.

"Wonderful. And I assume you've been practicing this in your store?" asked Dave.

"You bet. I've actually been practicing it at home as well," said Milo.

"Please tell me you don't practice on Isabel," said Dave.

"No, only the girls," Milo grinned. "Isabel is off limits. That would be reckless."

"Indeed," responded Dave.

It was a good place to break. Dave's brain was getting full, and both could see it.

"So where do we go from here?" asked Dave.

"We need a few conversations to get this fully fleshed out. And of course, we'll have to get it into our policies, once you approve. For now, let's just practice. Console the error, coach the at-risk, sanction the reckless, all independent of the outcome. Practice it on the road when you're watching the squirrelly behavior of other cars, practice on your kids, secretly practice it on Valerie, and watch us as your managers. And don't forget to watch the press. Sports stars, Hollywood celebrities, everyday Joes - it's a target-rich environment," said Milo.

"OK, that'll work. Anything else?" asked Dave.

"Yeah, try to notice the operation of your System 1 and System 2 brains. Watch in particular the operation of your risk monitor. Take note of when it goes off. Take note when it doesn't. And when Valerie gives you that look, that somehow you're just not seeing something you should see, ask why? Why did your risk monitor not alert you to something so visible to her? I'm convinced that risk monitor is central to any system of justice, workplace, societal, family. Keep an eye on how it works," said Milo.

"Wonderful. Milo, this is more than I was hoping for. I appreciate the work. And I will indeed practice," said Dave. "So what's on the agenda for our next session?"

"The body of work, and I need your blessing on a few ideas I have," said Dave.

"Sounds interesting. But I'm toast. We'll definitely look at that later. Right now, I want to have some fun with your team," said Dave as he pushed his chair back and walked toward Charles, Esther, and Bryce. It was Dave's style to spend a little time talking with each of the artisans when he came to the store. Once in a while he'd do it as a customer, ordering a sub while he talked to the artisan. A joke, a question about family, a jab at an artisan's favorite sports team. Dave made it a point to know his team, even as it grew. Dave would say, "they're not going to care about you, if you don't show you care about them."

THE PIT

Milo was convinced that it was all about systems and behaviors. And when Milo talked about behaviors, he really meant choices. Not the errors, the inadvertent things that his artisans did. He was not concerned about the one off roast beef instead of turkey; he was more concerned with why that error occurred, and that took him back to the systems built around his artisans and the choices his artisans made within those system. Were they following the routine that was expected within the system that Milo and his team had created?

It all led back to Alisha's error. She picked up the wrong roll out of the bread rack, and gave it to Patti Foster. Milo had known, prior to the event, how critical the gluten-free check really was.

Milo was even monitoring compliance with that out-loud check. Yet, Milo knew he was finding some level of non-compliance. He had observed the breach of a safety protocol and had been ineffective in stopping it before it led to the Patti Foster event.

It left Milo with a pit in the bottom of his stomach. "Why," he asked himself, "was it not me that Patti Foster wanted fired?" Milo was the manager. Milo was the one responsible for the outcomes of the store. He was the one largely responsible for the systems that the store employed to keep customers safe. Some of those simply came from other stores, from the home store, yet Milo felt responsible. Milo was beginning to believe that it was his responsibility to detect any drift into at-risk behavior.

Milo had a good friend from high school, Ellen, who had gone to law school. She was a criminal prosecutor, practicing across the river in Manhattan. Milo met Ellen for lunch one day to pick her brain about how much employers should be held responsible for the actions of their employees.

They ordered their lunches and got back to the conversation they'd already begun.

"Frolic?" asked Milo.

"Frolic. It's a funny legal term that addresses the sometimes crazy behavior of people while they're working," said Ellen.

"Say your garbage man decides to park his truck in front of a neighborhood pub, goes in for a few beers and winds up in a bar brawl with another patron over who has the best fans, the Yankees or the Red Sox. Your garbage man, a rabid Red Sox fan, takes one of those very heavy beer mugs and clunks the other guy upside the head. Should your garbage company be held liable for the frolic of their truck driver?" she asked.

"Well, that doesn't seem right. In that scenario, assuming this was the first time this driver had done something like this, I wouldn't expect the employer to be able to predict that this guy would do something so stupid. I wouldn't even really expect the employer to have an explicit rule about doing something like this because it's just so obviously wrong." Milo was thinking back to Fred writing "wow" on that woman's receipt. "You just can't expect an employer to cover every possible stupid employee act – there's just too much human variability."

"Exactly! The law recognizes that we can't control all the behaviors of our employees. If an employee goes off the rails and engages in some behavior that is clearly outside of his employment duties or the expectations of an employer, the law says we're not going to hold the employer liable," said Ellen. "It should be easy if you switch your thinking to off-hours conduct. I suspect you'd never expect to be held accountable if one of your employees robbed a bank off-hours?"

"Well, obviously if it's off-hours, the employer wouldn't be responsible – at least, not yet! But I'm still a little foggy about what employee behavior I'm responsible for on-hours? Say my employee does rob a bank on-hours? Am I responsible?"

"It comes down to scope," said Ellen. "When the courts have to judge employer liability, they look at whether the employee's behavior fell within the scope of what they were hired to do. Clearly, your garbage company didn't hire a driver to get into a bar brawl instead of picking up your trash. Nor would we expect them to have hired the driver to rob banks at night. So if you're wondering if you have some liability for an employee's actions, look at the activity they were engaged in, and ask yourself, 'was the activity within the scope of their employment?'"

Milo thanked Ellen for her very helpful legal clarifications. As he headed back to the store to help with closing, he thought again about the "wow" receipt. Milo felt no responsibility for Fred writing "wow" on the receipt of the attractive female customer, nor did he ever think he might be responsible for Fred's action. He didn't feel any responsibility for Charles's sit-in at the state house, either. Those were easy. No guilt on Milo's part. Humans will be human, and for Milo as a manager, there were limits around what conduct of others he should personally be responsible for.

But what about Alisha? It always seemed to come back to Alisha. Alisha was not on a frolic when she gave Patti Foster a gluten-rich roll. She was acting as manager, she was acting as an artisan, she was trying to help Fred with his irritated customer, she was doing her best to get her job done.

In addition, her fellow artisans had all, at some level, drifted away from the gluten-free check. The pace of the store, the pressure to meet the core measures, were all contributing factors to artisans skipping the check. The environment in which the artisans worked - that was Milo's responsibility - where he had control - and Dave's responsibility - he had set up the entire Dave's Subs system.

Milo could easily believe there were frolics that he as a manager should feel no responsibility for. At the other end of the spectrum was employee conduct for which he was entirely accountable. Milo drew that line at the inadvertent human errors that his artisans made. Milo agreed with Dave that a person should not be fired simply because they made mistake, no matter how awful the outcome. If we are inescapably fallible human beings, then when Milo hired a new artisan he was knowingly hiring on that fallibility, at least in the context of human errors. Milo wasn't yet ready to deal with the employee who was simply error-prone; that he would leave for later. He couldn't solve all the world's problems in one day!

Milo knew, though, that it was neither employee frolics nor employee errors that were creating the pit he had in his stomach. If Milo hired artisans cursed with inescapable fallibility, he knew those same artisans were blessed with free will. Even if, like him, System 1 was making many of their choices for them subconsciously, his artisans still made choices. Free will was simply part of the package when hiring humans. And if it was part of the package, it was Milo's responsibility to manage it.

Milo had come to believe that Patti Foster's calls for someone to be fired should have pointed at him. He was pushing production, as was every location of Dave's Subs, he did not intervene when he recognized his artisans were drifting from the gluten-free check. In fact, it was his responsibility to actively monitor whether his artisans were doing the check and if they weren't, to fix it before someone like Patti Foster got hurt.

Alisha had not been engaged in a frolic when she mistakenly grabbed the wrong roll. She was working within the scope of her employment. Monitoring the gluten-free check fell within the scope of *his* job duties...Patti Foster really should have called for his termination.

Milo was feeling pretty low. As they made their way to bed that night, Isabel was worried. "Honey, what's bothering you?" she asked.

"I have this pit in my stomach. And it's not something I ate. I've been thinking about Alisha's error, her failure to do the gluten-free check," said Milo.

"And what's bothering you now?" asked Isabel.

"What's bothering me is all of the focus that was pointed right toward Alisha. I was her manager. I knew that my artisans were sometimes not performing the gluten-free check. Yet, I let it go. I did not stop the at-risk behavior before it led to harm. Yet, everything after that event pointed right at Alisha. Patti Foster called for her termination. Alisha was the one who served the sub, she was the one right there at the front line, and as a result she was the target. None of us wanted what happened to Patti Foster to happen," said Milo.

"And you wanted the finger to point at you?"

"I think it should have," said Milo.

"Honey, did it matter if the finger pointed anywhere? Alisha, you, Dave's Subs, gave Patti Foster the wrong roll. And you paid a tremendous amount of money to settle the claim Patti Foster made. Dave, you, and Alisha all share the responsibility. Consider it shared accountability. I'm with you. You've convinced me that Alisha should not have been fired. I get that. But I don't think you should have been fired either. You're a great manager. You're trying your best, just like Alisha did," said Isabel.

"I know, but I could have prevented it," said Milo.

"I know that. And I know that Alisha could have prevented it. And I'm sure that there is something Dave could have done in how he set up the shop that could have prevented it. Remember, you're not going to be perfect. Just because you are the manager does not mean that anyone expects you to now be perfect. You're doing the right things. You're learning from Patti's event. You're going from being a good manager to being a great manager. Don't be so hard on yourself, honey" said Isabel.

Easy for Isabel to say. Hard for Milo to do. After six months, Milo felt worse about Alisha's event than he had when it happened. He knew something remained to allow him to put the Patti Foster event completely behind him. And it would not wait. He prepared for Monday morning at the store.

"Alisha, can I talk to you for a moment?" Milo asked.

"Sure, what's up?" Alisha responded.

Milo led her off to one of the tables toward the front of the store. Milo could see that Alisha was a little nervous by the look on her face.

"Alisha, I must say something to you that is long overdue. I apologize," said Milo.

"For what?" Alisha jumped in, confused.

"For letting you down in April. For not taking responsibility for what I owned in the Patti Foster event," said Milo.

"Wait, I don't get it. It was me who made the mistake. It was me that did not do the gluten-free check," said Alisha.

"I know. But I was your manager. I had a role to play, and in that, I failed. I failed Patti Foster. I failed you."

Her eyes told him she was not prepared for an apology. Months had passed since she'd made the mistake, but Alisha clearly still felt uneasy. She knew that there were a number of people, including a few artisans at other stores, who had wanted her fired. She knew Dave's Subs had chosen mercy in their response to her, that she was spared the penalty that employers usually give in these situations. Termination. For Alisha, this conversation had moved into the surreal.

"Alisha, it was my responsibility as the store manager to address the norm that I saw developing around the gluten-free check. Certainly, once I noticed you all drifting from the check, it was my job to work to correct it before it led to harm. I didn't do enough. And I am sorry for that. Please accept my apology," said Milo.

"Milo. I...I don't know what to say. I'm so confused. It really *was* me. I made the mistake. You're a great manager, and you and Dave went to bat for me in the aftermath of the event. I could not have asked for better bosses," said Alisha.

"Well, I just wanted you to know that I feel responsible for the event. I'm sorry," said Milo.

Now it was Alisha feeling bad. Not the sentiment that Milo had hoped to achieve.

"Milo, you need to know that what you and Dave did has had impact well beyond what you might realize," said Alisha. "The grace that you showed me, your support in the face of my screwup? It has changed my family. We're more forgiving. My own mother has more tolerance now. My friends see the world differently. It was as if what you and Dave did gave them hope of a more forgiving spirit in the world. We live in a world that just wants to point the finger when somebody messes up, as if that solves anything. You guys decided not to do that. And it's made a difference ever since. Me, my family, and my friends will never be the same because of what you and Dave have done."

The pit in Milo's stomach was gone. Milo had said what he needed to say; he had owned his piece of what Isabel had called shared accountability. Alisha had repaid him with a wonderful testimony about the impact of Dave's decision not to fire her for a mistake. It filled Milo with continued hope that he was on the right path.

Yet, Milo knew, as did Dave, that this tolerance for shared humanity – and accountability - would have to yield results. Another Patti Foster event would have the hardliner's coming out of the woodwork asking for the head of the last person to touch whatever it was that was now broken. Dave and Milo both believed that this new approach was the right thing to do. They just needed to prove it before the press was given a chance to kill it.

Dave had made the decision not to terminate Alisha and it was Dave who had written the letter to employers, but it was Milo he tasked with operationalizing the letter. That meant Milo had to be proactive. He needed his team to report what he couldn't see - as Bryce and Fred had when they'd returned from the park dedication. He needed a strong learning culture. Milo needed to be watching, to head off any at-risk behaviors before they led to harm. And he would have to continuously re-evaluate his system design. He needed to be better than the rest. As with any attempt to change the culture, he had to demonstrate that it would, in the end, produce better results. People were watching.

POTPOURRI

Dave was intrigued by where Milo took the meat slicer event. Or, perhaps, he was intrigued by where he himself did not take the event. Dave felt duped. Not by Robin, his manager at Store #1, more by his own willingness to slip to re-training as a solution before Robin had even investigated a cause of the event. Milo had convinced Dave that the search for cause, however imperfect that search, should always precede the identification of corrective or preventive strategies. Digging deeper opened doors to solutions that he would never see otherwise.

All of his managers got the email. In 30 days, Dave was hosting a safety meeting in the aftermath of the meat slicer event. The email was short:

Title: Review of Safety Events
When: Saturday, 9:00 – 10:30 am
Where: Store #1
Please come prepared to discuss the safety events you have
had at your stores in this last year.

Thirty days later, the managers gathered at Store #1, not because it was the original, but because it was centrally located. Dave brought donuts and coffee. For those, like Milo, who didn't drink coffee, Dave offered the standard juices and sodas that Dave's Subs offered to its customers.

Dave jumped right into the meeting with little in the way of introduction.

"So, I was impressed by our ability to learn from the meat slicer event. And Milo's diagramming of the Patti Foster event was great. Now, I want to up the ante," said Dave.

"Up the ante?" responded Robin, Store #1 manager.

"Yes. I want us to see what we can learn from the totality of the events we had last year. Hits, like the Patti Foster event, and near misses, the ones only you would know from your own store," said Dave.

Dave gave his managers fifteen minutes to write down the safety events they had within their six respective stores. He wanted one-liners. And in many cases, the managers had come prepared with their list of events and near misses.

"Good," Dave said when he saw that they were finished. "Now, pass your list to the person on your right."

Milo was on Robin's right and he found himself staring at her list. Andre, on Milo's right, had Milo's list.

"What do you see?" asked Dave. "Do you see any trends? Do you see anything common between your list and that of the store you're managing?"

Everyone seemed to think this was a good exercise, particularly when they saw the similarity among the lists.

"So they're pretty similar," said Andre.

"Yeah, you'd think we were all in same business," added Dave drily, knowing that if he didn't say it, one of his managers would.

"So what do we do with this data?" asked Robin.

"Seems like if we fix this stuff, we'll be good," added Andre.

"Nothing," said Milo.

It was as if the power had gone out in the movie theatre, stopping right in the middle of all the action. No outrage from those sitting around the table, just stunned silence.

Then, "what do you mean do nothing?" asked Robin.

"These are outcomes. Look at the list," said Milo. "You got things like customer tripped and fell, artisan smashed hand, water line broke, freezer contaminated."

"Yeah?" said another manager.

"They're good to know. These lists tell us what's happening," said Milo. "They can help us prioritize what we're doing, where we focus our attention. But what we need, in addition to this, is the data on *why* these things are occurring. The systems and the behaviors that lead to these undesired safety events. It's the systems and behaviors that we can manage. The outcomes, well, we just get to watch those. And that's why I said we do nothing. Until we get the causal data."

Dave jumped in. "Milo is right. Getting at the causal data helps us really look at and fine-tune our systems," said Dave. "We can't know where our systems need fine tuning until we know where, and more importantly, *how* and *why* they're breaking down."

"It doesn't matter whether we're looking at customer satisfaction, or employee safety, or artisans meeting our subs-per-rush core measure," said Milo. "We're not digging so that we're better able to blame somebody for the failure. We're digging so that we can figure out if the system contributed to the event or whether an artisan made an at-risk or reckless choice, or more likely, where system and artisan need to share accountability. But not so we can fire people. So we can learn! If we don't have an environment in which we learn from this list of bad outcomes we've generated, then the list is a waste."

Milo looked at Robin. "You all know what I'm saying is true. Hard, perhaps, but true. What good did it do for us to say, 'oops, an artisan sliced her hand open on the meat slicer and ended up with fourteen stitches – so sad, so sorry.' I wasn't willing to leave it to retraining and crossing my fingers hoping that it wouldn't happen again – at least not on my watch. Neither were you."

"We had a duty to our artisans to learn from this incident and do our best to implement changes that prevented, or at least decreased the likelihood that another artisan would slice their hand open. We have to do the same thing with the other items on this list!"

Milo had become a convert to Dave's philosophy around human error. But Dave himself had no idea where it would take Milo. Dave didn't know that his letter would inspire Milo to look at system reliability or at shared accountability, or go off on that crazy System 1/System 2 tangent to figure out how people made decisions, or invent that – what did Milo call it? - that risk monitor. In his search for a new, more humane system of accountability, Milo was finding the secrets to organizational performance. Design good systems; help employees make good choices within those systems. That was it. Milo had found the Holy Grail, and Dave was becoming a believer.

Upsetting Esther

Six months into managing the new store. Milo had weathered the storm of the Patti Foster event. He'd briefed Dave on his findings, his new model of the three behaviors, human error, at-risk and reckless. Milo was feeling pretty good about his progress. That is, until Esther spoke to a friend, an artisan at another store.

"I need to talk to you."

Esther didn't look happy. "Can it wait until after the rush is over?" asked Milo.

"So what's up?" asked Milo as the rush wound down.

"I want to know how you decided our raises," said Esther.

"Ok, what do you want to know?" asked Milo scrambling to buy time so he could respond well to Esther's indelicately put question.

"Well, I spoke with Syd at Store #5. Syd told me he got a 6% raise. His raise was based on his production. He's the fastest guy at Store #5. How'd you decide on mine?"

"Well, I don't usually talk about other people's raises with employees, but in this case, I don't think it matters if I tell you," said Milo. "Dave gave me a raise pool and I spread it evenly among all Store #6 artisans."

"How'd you come up with that plan?" asked Esther, clearly agitated.

"Well, I didn't actually spend a lot of time thinking about the raises. I guess I was more focused on trying to recover from the business hit we took with Patti Foster…"

"Yeah, that was Alisha's fault," interrupted Esther.

Milo's look let Esther know that she was getting awfully close to a line she should probably not cross.

"And, I suppose I was thinking that you all started at the same time…I wasn't really thinking about this in terms of performance," said Milo.

"Obviously," said Esther. "Look, I don't mean to be rude. But I've been hustling for the past six months. I pump out more subs than anybody else here. And I still manage to be friendly." Esther took a breath. "I talked to Alisha about it. She wasn't incredibly sympathetic. She's just happy to still have her job. But she doesn't really think it's fair either that Fred and Charles move like slugs while she and I look like we've run a marathon after 90 minutes. Just doesn't seem fair that we're all rewarded the same when clearly our performances are different! My raise actually feels like a punishment to me."

Milo didn't know what to say, so that's what he told Esther. He promised that he would take some time to consider what she had presented to him and get back to her within the week.

Esther looked like she would have preferred a more immediate response, but knew she had perhaps pressed her luck already on the raise issue. "I can wait a week," she said as she swung her backpack over her shoulder and headed out the door.

Milo watched her walk away. For the past four months he'd been focused solely on single events, and how he should manage those. Esther, understandably, was focused on production. From her perspective, production was the more important issue of the two. For the moment, Milo had dodged the Esther bullet. He knew, though, that she'd be back in a week, looking for satisfaction. That didn't give him a lot of time.

Milo was a big sports fan. He knew that some players were better at their respective games than others. "Wow, just take a look at his talent!" he might say. Likewise, he'd see a particular player that seemed to be trying really hard, yet not producing very good results. "Well, you have to give him an E for effort" Milo might say. There were clearly jobs where extra talent and extra effort did result in better results. Professional sports, in particular, seemed designed to find and highlight those differences. Strangely, Dave' Subs, during the lunchtime rush, seemed designed to do the same. And if better athletes made much more money than merely average athletes, why was that not true at Dave's Subs, wondered Milo?

Milo could see that there were jobs in the world where the differences between employees were less visible by design. Being a commercial pilot seemed one of those jobs. Being a commercial airline pilot, an occupation Milo thoroughly respected, was clearly a difficult task. It took years of training to gain proficiency. Milo knew that commercial pilots were required to have thousands of hours of experience before they were allowed to fly commercial jumbo jets. That said, once all of the training was complete, and with thousands of hours of competency building, piloting an aircraft was routine.

Esther, giving it her all for 90 minutes of a rush looked more strung out at the end of that 90 minutes than a pilot who just finished a flight from Newark to Chicago O'Hare. And that was a good thing. No one wants her airline captain to look like it took every ounce of skill he could muster to just get that airplane from Newark to Chicago!

Once trained, transporting passengers safely on an aircraft should be well within the skill set of even the lowest performing pilot. After all, we don't arrive at the gate asking that only the first string pilot be in command of our aircraft. The flying public is not willing to pay more for the first string pilot. When an airline chooses a pilot for a commercial flight, passengers expect a minimum level of competency that includes departing from one location and landing safely in the next. Additionally, passengers fully expect that the pilot will not face any circumstances during the flight that will require tremendous effort on the pilot's part. Generally, on an airplane flight, as in our daily commutes in our automobiles, if heroics have been necessary, something has gone dreadfully wrong! A great touchdown reception by a wide receiver might involve seemingly super-human skill. The safe landing of an aircraft had better not require extraordinary skill. Unlike baseball where we can compare batting stats, there are some jobs where we simply do not want employees to distinguish themselves, aircraft pilot being one.

Milo knew that being a sub artisan was a job where artisans could indeed excel in relation to their peers. Esther produced 85 subs per 90-minute rush, well beyond the minimum, and well beyond some of her fellow artisans at store #6. Should she be rewarded for that output? Milo thought she should.

Better production should equal better pay as long as other Dave's Subs values were not being compromised. That's the capitalist part of employment in America, at least for the jobs where distinguishing yourself from the pack matters.

Milo found the best examples for thinking through how to reward fairly for performance in the arts and in sports. In those two areas, athletes and artists - musicians, writers and movie stars - could differentiate themselves from the pack, and be paid well – and differently - for doing so.

A simple equation took shape in Milo's head:

$$TALENT + CHOICES + LUCK = OUTCOMES$$

It had been spinning around in his head, in some form, since he was a high schooler. Milo was decent at sports, and excelled at music. He had talent, enough that he had seriously considered pursuing a career as a professional musician. Milo could see something similar in his favorite athletes and artists; many of them had what appeared as either natural talents, or talents borne of hard work put in well before Milo ever heard of them.

Watching athletes and artists, Milo was well aware of the amount of time and energy needed to hone their craft. Choice, too, played a role, Milo knew – how much practice time was an individual athlete or artist willing to put in? A star athlete who, after putting in extra effort in the off-season, reviewing game films on the weekend during the season, and then in the game, made consistently better choices than his peers due, in part, to his innate talent and greatly to his choice to spend extra time practicing and reviewing the films? Choice surely mattered.

And then there was luck. There are a lot of good musicians out there, and a lot of good athletes. No matter how good his natural or developed talents, no matter how hard he tried in the moment, there was that issue of luck. Luck might be a career ending injury, as Milo knew so well, or just a career-ending mistake made at the most inopportune time. Or luck might be bumping into a famous music producer in line at the local Starbucks on a day she was in a talkative mood.

Now giving it some thought, Milo believed that he should compensate his employees for the talent they brought to Dave's Subs, and for the choices they made while on the clock. Luck, he thought, should be pulled from the calculus of compensation. Over time, Milo knew, luck would equalize across his sub artisans. With a large enough data set, Milo could measure the performance of employees by their outcomes, by the number of subs per rush they pushed out the door.

There may have been individual days where Fred or Charles outperformed Esther and Alisha. Yet, over time Fred's lack of production became clear. Esther and Alisha were the top performers at Store #6. The outcome measure of subs per lunchtime rush was a good proxy for their talent and choices. Esther was right. She had talent and hustle, and she chose to apply that talent and hustle at Dave's Subs. She made subs fast, and her customers appreciated it.

Talent, choices, and luck, those were the ingredients for producing results. Esther certainly wasn't claiming that luck contributed to her subs per rush measure, nor was she really suggesting she was more talented at putting meat, cheese and veggies on a bread roll. What she did believe was that she chose to really hustle during the rush and that her hustle, her *choice* to hustle, should be rewarded. Esther delivered sub production for Dave's Subs; she wanted Dave's Subs on their part, to deliver just compensation. Milo could not disagree. He set up a call with Dave.

"Dave, I need your help," said Milo.

"What do you need?" asked Dave.

"My top performer is grumbling. She wants to be compensated for her higher level of production. She's had a conversation with an artisan at another store and with one at mine. She knows at least some of our stores compensate based on their subs per rush number. I tried to put her off, at first. I told her other people's raises were generally not up for discussion. I explained that we'd all been focused on the Patti Foster event, and told her that because all the artisans at Store #6 had started at the same time, we had decided to spread the raises evenly. I also assured her that we planned a thorough performance review at one year. She thought it was kinda lame that we were waiting an entire year to recognize a good performer. And, frankly, I think she raises a good point. A year is a long time to wait in the restaurant industry," said Milo

"I'm pulling up your stats now. Esther and Alisha are the top two performers, by a long shot," said Dave.

"Yeah, based upon the core measure, they are," said Milo.

"Let's go ahead and give them each a 5% bump," said Dave. "Look, it's been a tough start at your store, the whole Patti Foster thing. Esther and you are probably right. A strong performer shouldn't have to wait an entire year to be recognized for their value to Dave's Subs."

"Thank you! I'm glad you agree and I know it will go a long way with Esther and Alisha. You should know that Alisha didn't raise the issue. Esther said she's still just feeling grateful to have a job after the Patti Foster deal. I'll talk to both of them both. And thank you, again," said Milo.

"No worries," said Dave. "I'm glad you brought it to my attention."

Movie Night, Again

Every year, around the holiday season, Milo's family gets together to watch Frank Capra's *It's a Wonderful Life*. It was his mother's favorite movie. Milo's two sisters, their families, and his family would join Milo's parents at a local movie theatre that presented the holiday classic every year. Milo's mother cooked the same pot of homemade noodles, and afterwards, the family would head out to the theater, filled to bursting, for the show.

Milo and his father always tried to sit as far away from each other as they could. This was a deliberate strategy for them, because at the end of the movie, his father always burst into tears and that was all it took for Milo's own tears to flow. Watching a grown man cry or being a grown man sobbing like a baby did not match up with their definition of manly men. Regardless of where they sat, their strategy always failed – and usually ended in hysterical laughing through their tears - for both of them.

The movie touched upon human fallibility. In fact, the rights to the movie itself was a story of human fallibility. Frank Capra, the producer, forgot to extend the copyright, inadvertently allowing the copyright to lapse, and thereby releasing the movie into the public domain. It is considered by many to be Frank Capra's unintentional gift to the world.

The movie traces the early 1900s life of George Bailey, the oldest son of Pa Bailey, the owner of Bailey Savings and Loan. With his father's passing, George gives up his dream of traveling the world and building skyscrapers and bridges and takes on the task of managing the savings and loan. Every decision George makes running the Bailey Savings and Loan reflects a genuine concern for those in the community, even his declining the high paying offer to join Mr. Potter, the evil owner of the town's only bank, to stay with the "penny ante savings and loan" as he'd once referred to it in a conversation with his father.

Central to the story is his forgetful and somewhat inept Uncle Billy, George's second in command at the Bailey Savings and Loan. At the midpoint in the story, Uncle Billy loses $8000 on the way to make a deposit at Potter's bank. When the loss is discovered, George desperately tells Uncle Billy, "Someone's going to go to jail and it's not going to be me."

On the verge of throwing himself from the bridge into the icy waters below, George instead finds himself rescuing what turns out to be his guardian angel, Clarence, tasked with saving George as a prerequisite for finally getting his angel's wings. As they're warming themselves, Clarence tells George why he's there. When George remarks that it probably would have been better if he'd never been born, Clarence decides to show him just what the world would have been like without him.

This year, Milo and Isabel were unable to attend the family gathering to watch *It's a Wonderful Life* with Milo's parents. Not wanting to miss out entirely, Isabel had chosen the holiday classic for their movie night, knowing that its warm message would help get them both in the holiday spirit.

Girls to bed, sodas poured, popcorn popped, Milo and Isabel snuggled in for the movie. Sure enough, exactly two hours and eight minutes later, with just two minutes left, Milo burst into tears. His father was not there. He had no excuses. This was all on him.

While George was discovering, with Clarence's help, what the world would have been like without him, George' wife, Mary, was marshaling his friends to come to his aid. It was George for whom the arrest warrant had been issued; it was he as President of the Bailey Savings and Loan, who would pay the price for Uncle Billy's misplacement of the $8000.

They came out in force to help, gathering in George and Mary's living room, bringing what they could to help, which ended up being significantly more than the missing $8000. At the end of the movie, George and his friends break out singing *Auld Lang Syne*. George, holding his youngest daughter in his arms, glances down at the pile of money on the table. His eye catches something on top of the pile, and he reaches down for it. It is Clarence's copy of *Tom Sawyer*, a book Clarence had been reading throughout his assignment with George. George opened it to find an inscription written inside: "Dear George, remember no man is a failure who has friends. Thanks for the wings, Love Clarence."

It's at this point in the movie, a repeatable, precise mechanism out of Milo's control that Milo bursts into tears. Isabel knew it was coming. She knew Milo was following in his Dad's footsteps - the older he got, the more sentimental he became.

It's a Wonderful Life was a parable and as a parable was more than entertainment. It attempted to teach. Frank Capra's gift to the world was not lost on Milo. He'd seen the movie over a dozen times. Yet, this time was different. If ever there was a movie aligned with Dave's letter to his employees, it was this one.

Uncle Billy had made a mistake, losing control of $8000, a significant amount of money at the time. The police were called, the press was called. Mr. Potter himself actually had the money; he'd found it inside the newspaper Uncle Billy was reading before he handed it to Potter, but he chose to stand by and watch as the "system" came after George Bailey.

As the manager of the Bailey Savings and Loan, George took responsibility for Uncle Billy's mistake even though he knew he had little to do with it. That's just the way the system worked. With all of the sacrifices that George Bailey had made for the people around him, his family and his community, he thought he was only as good as this most recent banking deposit – or lack of one. George Bailey lived in a world poised and ready to devour anyone who committed a wrong - or so he thought. The outpouring of love, the caring of his community, took George Bailey – and Mr. Potter – by surprise.

Milo had heard of the term "body of work," perhaps from Dave himself. It had never really meant much to him, until now. The moral of *It's a Wonderful Life* was that George Bailey had built up an incredible body of work. He was selfless his entire life, living in service to others. George had set aside his own aspirations for education, for travel, for glory, out of love for others. And when he was implicated in a mistake, the loss of $8000, all Mary needed to do was tell George Bailey's friends that he was in trouble. It was George Bailey's body of work that defined him. Not one event. Not one mistake. Not one oversight. Not one at-risk behavior. But by an entire body of work. George Bailey was more than his last mistake. Just as Dave wanted to be more than his last trade or Alisha more than that poisonous sub for Patti Foster.

Milo had spent the last ten months or so figuring out how to address the single event. He knew what workplace justice should look like in the single event. And then Esther brought up the core performance measure for every artisan – how fast an artisan can produce subs – raising the issue of fairness around how artisans should be compensated.

Milo saw where he next needed to set his sights - toward the body of work. If workplace justice wasn't just about that last bad event, then it wasn't just about meeting the core measure of subs per rush. The lesson of *It's a Wonderful Life*, Milo now saw clearly, was that justice had to look at the whole, at the body of work.

An Injury-Free Workplace

It began with a call from Dave.

"Milo, I want to run something by you," said Dave.

"Sure, what is it?" replied Milo turning off the meat slicer.

"I've been talking to an old friend of mine," said Dave.

Milo knew this meant as much trouble for him as when he called Dave and said he'd been talking to a friend. It seemed that whenever either one of them talked to an old friend, it meant some change was ahead for Dave's Subs. Milo prepared himself.

"He works at a local manufacturing plant. They've been working on industrial accident rates. You know, lost workday injuries," said Dave.

"Sure, I get the idea," interjected Milo.

"They have been changing systems and procedures. You know, making the job site safer. But they realize it also requires employees to make safe choices within the system management has created," said Dave.

"Still hanging with you," said Milo.

"So here's the thing," said Dave. "They've created a program to reward safe behavior. If a local group or team goes the quarter without an injury, they get a bonus. Something like $50 added to their paycheck."

"And you want to do that here at Dave's Subs?" asked Milo, cautiously.

"Yeah, but before I do, I thought I'd check with you to see if you thought it was a good idea," said Dave.

"Well, I'd have to give it some thought," said Milo.

"People make mistakes, sure. We're not talking about firing anyone here. But is it wrong to reward those who can go a quarter without an injury?" said Dave.

"Can you give me a day or two to think about it?" asked Milo.

"Fair enough," said Dave.

Milo wondered if he was going to lose Dave's confidence always taking time to think through the issues Dave raised. Some questions should be simple. It shouldn't take a day or two to develop an answer for a seemingly simple question. For now, Dave was giving Milo some space.

Milo went back to slicing smoked ham, thinking about Dave's proposal. Would it be fair to reward stores who went a quarter without injury? Immediately Milo went back to his team. He'd only been open for nine months, but Milo himself had a slightly crushed finger from a customer who closed the store door on him when he wasn't looking. Bryce sliced his finger on the sharp grated edge of the plastic wrap holder. And, of course, there were Fred's two injured ribs as a result of the skateboard accident.

Did Milo's store go 90 days without an injury during the nine months it had been open? No. Maybe Dave was talking only about injuries where the employee lost a full day of work? Was this about the injury, or the ability of Milo's team to work through the injury that mattered? For Milo, Dave's simple question opened a can of wiggling, squirmy worms.

Alisha, Esther, and Charles did not have any injury during that first six months of work. Did that mean they were safer employees than Dave, Bryce, and Fred? Or, were they just luckier?

Sure, there might be data suggesting that one employee was less safe than another. Perhaps if Fred had had all three of the injuries on three separate occasions, Milo should consider him as unsafe. Would three events in 9 months now be statistically reliable enough to conclude that Fred was lacking, either in a safety gene or in the choices he made? If that had been the case, should Milo then take action with Fred, at least to understand why the trend was occurring, understanding the risk that going down that path might lead to a decision that Fred was too unsafe to work at Dave's Subs?

And there were more considerations. If everyone else had gotten through 6 months without an injury, why should they be penalized for Fred's injuries? Milo was becoming more confused the more he thought about the Dave's proposal. His food prep had slowed to almost nothing as his System 2 brain was consumed by the workplace injury question. To be efficient, and to be safe, Milo decided to focus solely on the meat slicer and leave the workplace injury question for later.

It was a good day at the store. "No injuries," Milo thought to himself, a slight grin on his face. "Only eighty-nine more to go." Milo was back on task, thinking about whether teams should be rewarded for a "zero injury" quarter. He worried that this was a back-door way of expecting perfection from his artisans.

It didn't take long for Milo to recognize that his discomfort with Dave's proposal came down to statistics and luck. Milo had long since come to the decision that he must absolutely hold employees accountable for their choices. Additionally, Dave and he worked diligently to refine and keep their systems up to date – the change to the plastic glove policy was one clear example of updating their system based on new information or technologies.

He asked his employees to make good choices in the systems Dave and he designed. What result should they expect? Well, regardless of how good their system was, Milo's team was still fallible. Alisha's error would not go away. He was stuck with inherent and inescapable human fallibility. This meant he would occasionally be stuck with bad outcomes.

It was another epiphany for Milo. Flawed human beings, no matter how assembled, would occasionally produce flawed results. Perfection would not be possible, for single humans, or for teams as a whole.

Milo knew he and Dave should judge outcomes – good and bad - cautiously, doing their best not to create expectations of perfection. In football, only one team can win the Super Bowl each year. But that doesn't mean the best team always wins; only that the winning team had it all come together on the big day, or at a minimum, didn't make many blunders. The right talent, the right choices as a team, and a little luck, and a team won the Super Bowl.

Workplace teams were no different. A bit of talent to begin, although Milo could see no obvious talent differences from store to store. Choices, well, those may be different from store to store. Some teams might be drifting into unsafe choices more than others, but that seemed both an employee and management issue. Lastly, though, was a bit of luck. Outcomes were the product of talent, system design and the choices of the humans working within those systems, and a bit of luck.

Milo thought he had it figured out. What made it a statistics problem was the problem of a too small sample size. Milo considered his beloved baseball. A team that went 102 – 60 was better than a team that went 60 – 102. Over the course of a season with this number of games, luck worked its way out of the equation. A baseball team that wins 102 games in a season is indeed a better team than one that wins only 60. On the other hand, if a team played only one game, whether they won or lost would tell a fan little about how good the team was going to be for the season.

The problem with workplace injuries, particularly in a small business like Dave's Subs is that the numerator was so small. Zero injuries versus one injury. Zero injuries meant a bonus, and one injury meant no bonus. Milo was struggling with the real difference between a team that had one injury and a team that had none. After all he'd learned over the past nine months, Milo suspected that human error and luck probably accounted for any difference in rate. Did the team with no injuries really have more talent and make better choices? Milo was not convinced. The presence of a single injury was just not a meaningful indicator of workplace safety. Nor, for that matter, was the absence of a single injury.

For the injury rate to be meaningful, Milo needed more data. He needed to know what those teams were doing. He wanted to see the choices of his team members. *That* would be a more reliable indicator of his team's commitment to workplace safety.

Milo also struggled with what the measure would mean to the culture in his store. If someone were injured, would they choose not to report it in order to save a chance at the bonus? Milo had seen headlines of companies prosecuted for hiding state-reportable injuries. Milo knew that humans would quickly learn to play the safety game as designed. Give people the target of zero injuries, and they'd work hard to get there, particularly with a monetary incentive. Milo didn't want to give an incentive to his team to hide adverse events.

The problem, as Milo saw it, was not with rewarding employees for being safe. It was the target itself, the measure – zero injuries. One unlucky moment, perhaps even something out of his employees' control, like his own finger crushed in a door by a harried customer, made the difference between a bonus and no bonus.

Milo didn't have all of the answers, and he knew it. He was still learning, and still working through what it meant to be accountable in the workplace. He had thought through the injury bonus, however, and was ready to speak with Dave.

"Ok, Dave, I have an answer for you."

"Let's hear it," said Dave.

"I don't think you should reward an injury free team," responded Milo, with some hesitation.

"Why?" Dave quickly asked.

"Because it rewards the wrong thing," responded Milo. "It mostly rewards luck, rather than choices."

"I'm only sort of tracking," responded Dave.

"We want our employees to make safe choices," said Milo. "And by making safe choices, we get better outcomes."

"Right," said Dave. "So what's the problem then?"

"The problem is the difference between zero injuries and one injury," responded Milo. "You were a securities trader. You made good trades and bad ones, I'm sure."

"Yeah," said Dave. "Sometimes, we made terrible ones."

"And remember what you told me after Alisha's event?" asked Milo. "Something like, you're only as good as your last trade? That's the problem with the injury measure. The difference between a good team deserving a bonus and a bad team undeserving of a bonus, in a company as small as yours, is a single injury. And mind you, that injury might very well have been out of the control of the team. Think terrible system design at Pablo's or just bad luck, like that customer who let go of the door while my finger was still in it, or even, to some extent, a mechanical failure like with our meat slicer."

"Ok, so what would you suggest?" asked Dave.

"Find a way to track our choices. It's a much more statistically reliable data set. Audit our stores. Send in someone we don't even know. Buy 10 subs at each store and watch what our employees do," said Milo, on the fly not having given that suggestion much System 2 thought.

Dave was silent, thinking about what Milo had said.

"I don't want one of my team members having the incentive to hide an injury to protect the bonus the team might have received that quarter if they'd been injury free," added Milo.

"Well, when you put it that way...Ok, we'll dump the idea of the injury-free workplace bonus," said Dave.

"Thank you," said Milo.

"You know, you're getting pretty smart about this stuff," said Dave.

"I've been thinking about this stuff a lot. The problem is that for every answer I find, I find two additional questions," said Milo.

Milo left his conversation with Dave feeling he'd won a small victory for the workplace. Not that it was a fight, but it felt like the more Milo thought through these ideas, the more he learned, the more he felt himself at odds with conventional business wisdom.

The bonus for an injury-free workplace would have made total sense to him six months or nine months ago. Now, it left him unsettled. Dave encouraged his managers to shoot down his ideas if they thought they were bad ideas. But he knew Dave was going to want a real alternative. The auditing was only the start. Milo knew Dave would come back to push the idea of incentives and their effectiveness. It would be on Milo's radar going forward.

THE CORE MEASURE

To the best of Milo's knowledge, nothing in Dave's letter after Alisha's event impacted what Dave referred to as his "core measures." Across the stores, Dave tracked two pieces of data on every sub artisan: the number of subs prepared during the lunch rush from 11:30 – 1:00, and the number of customers returning to each artisan (data taken from receipts). Dave tracked these at the store level, as a measure of store performance, and at the individual artisan level as a measure of artisan performance.

For Milo, the core measures presented two managerial dilemmas. First, what should he do with employees who did not meet the minimum expectation? And, second, what should he do with employees who greatly exceeded minimum expectations, a question Esther had brought rather forcefully to his attention when she expressed her dissatisfaction with Milo's peanut butter spread of the first round of raises at Store #6?

Dave had set the standard of 60 subs per lunch rush when he'd opened his first location; this number had not changed in the six years Dave's Subs had been opened for business. He was a process guy - believing that if his artisans could produce (fast and friendly), his business would grow. Subs per rush was the single most important criteria of success for a sub artisan. And it was the single most important criteria for success at the store level, a measure of a manager's effectiveness in running a store.

As Milo watched his artisans begin their prep work for the day's rush, he knew he had one employee who was not meeting core measure expectations and another who was just barely hitting the target.

Charles. He was at 57 subs per rush, having dropped in production after his initial improvement immediately after Milo's earlier conversation with him. And Fred. Fred, the jokester was at 63 subs per rush. Neither of them were stellar performers; Charles was not even meeting the minimum.

The rest of the team far exceeded the 60 subs per rush rate. Esther was a rock star at 85. Not only did the subs fly out of her station, she also had a very high rate of return customers. Alisha was another star performer at 83 subs per rush. And Bryce looked good, consistently pushing 72 subs out the door during a rush.

As an employer or manager, there is really only one reason to take on the expense of an employee – to have them produce. Whether they produce sub sandwiches, spreadsheets, or widgets, or whether they are strictly part of a sales force, the object of the employment game is to produce. Whether it's a capitalist marketplace or a socialist system, everybody, or nearly everybody, needs to produce to make it work.

Milo could do the numbers in his head. Charles and Fred were a real drag on the store's numbers. Two hundred workday lunches – Alisha and Esther outperforming Charles and Fred by 52 subs per day - that came to more than 10,000 subs, well over $60,000 in lost revenue for Dave's Subs each year. Two underperforming employees clearly were having a significant impact on Store #6's performance, not to mention the potential hit to morale.

Esther, producing 63% more subs than the lowest performer, Charles, visibly hustled. Charles looked like he was working in slow motion when compared side by side with Esther and Alisha. And Fred...every time Milo glanced in his direction, it seemed Fred and his customer were enjoying a good laugh. The trouble was that Fred always seemed to have stopped moving his hands - building subs - while he was laughing. Probably why Fred was barely meeting the minimum.

Milo had spent the 4th of July at Nathan's famous hot dog eating contest on Coney Island. ESPN covers the annual event as spectators in the crowd and at home sitting on their couches wait for the answer to the critical question: just how many hot dogs can one human being eat in 10 minutes? Nathan's brilliant contest (in marketing terms) is the eating equivalent of a sprint. Whoever is fastest at getting the most hot dogs in – and keeping them down – wins.

Having been confronted by Esther over the raises, Milo had already recognized the aspirational quality of the core measure. Employees *could* perform better than the expectation. In this area, employees could excel. And just as Nathan's Hot Dogs' contestants were compensated – or not – based on the number of hot dogs they could consume in ten minutes, sub artisans could be compensated commensurate with the number of subs they made in a ninety minute rush.

It was clear at Milo's store – Esther made more money for the store than did Charles or Fred. But being a sub artisan was a job, not a sporting event, or an eating spectacle. Milo had been thinking about workplace justice long enough that he knew there should be some limits around the core measure to ensure that it was a fair thing by which to measure artisans.

The first, he thought, related to reasonableness. If Dave had set the expectation at 200 subs per rush, not a single artisan could meet it. An impossible to achieve expectation made no business sense and certainly, was not fair. Furthermore, Milo was faced with five artisans, four of whom could meet the expectation, and one who could not. Did the fact that one or more artisans could produce within the expectation prove the expectation was reasonable?

Subs-per-hour was a measure of output over time. Milo saw this rate-based measure as a numerator and a denominator. Some hours, the rate would be higher than average, at other times lower. Just a few finicky customers could kill the stats from a single lunch rush. Given enough rushes, though, luck would work itself out of each artisan's subs per rush rate. So while it was likely unfair to hold an artisan accountable for their rate on a particular lunch rush, over time, it was a reasonable measure of artisan performance.

Different somewhat from reasonable, the core measure also needed to be possible. Milo could quickly see that having a store in an area that didn't support a good lunchtime rush just might make it impossible for any of the artisans to meet the minimum expectation, no matter how reasonable. So, too, could bad food or bad press – as in the Patti Foster event. No matter how good

Esther was, she would not be able to overcome a slow dribble of customers. In order to get to 85 subs per rush, she needed to average at least 85 customers per lunch rush – anything less and it would be impossible for her to reach 85.

Next, if the measure were reasonable and possible, it was only fair that Milo's artisans actually knew of the expectation. There was nothing fair about holding someone accountable for something of which they had no knowledge. Milo could imagine his artisans' response if the first time they were made aware of the subs per rush measure was at their first performance review – or when they were terminated for not meeting it. In fact, the measure was so core to Dave's Subs that Milo mentioned it several times during every interview, before a job offer had even been tendered. He only wanted to hire artisans who were clear on the need to hustle at Dave's Subs - that it was so critical, that Dave's Subs actually measured it.

And this took him right back to Charles. When Milo interviewed Charles, he looked across the interview table and immediately saw a very nice guy. Just as quickly, Milo registered that Charles was old. Right there in the interview, Milo thought to himself, "Can this guy keep up the pace?" Milo knew that not only could he not ask the question "was Charles too old to keep up," he wasn't even supposed to think it. At the same time, Milo knew that keeping up really wasn't necessarily a function of age; Milo had worked with plenty of 20 and 30 something sluggards in his food service experience.

Charles was older, that was a fact that neither Charles nor Milo could change. While Milo would not discriminate against Charles because of his age by assuming he could not keep up, he did press Charles, as he did all prospective employees, about the environment he was hoping to work in, impressing upon Charles the sprint-like nature of the lunch rush and that Dave's Subs measured the sprint. Charles convinced Milo that he would make a good sub artisan and that he would enjoy sprinting for an hour and a half each day.

Milo liked Charles and saw a wisdom and peace in him that probably came from his years as a schoolteacher. The answer to his question regarding Charles or any potential employee – could he keep up the pace for the length of his time at Dave's Subs – could only be discovered over time. Dave's Subs had no "sub-making" test for Milo to administer. As with any sub artisan, Milo trained Charles and then waited to see how he did.

In the subs per rush measure, Fred was right behind Charles, each battling for who could produce the fewest number of subs in a lunchtime rush. At 26, Fred was relatively young; at 66, Charles was relatively old. These two artisans quickly confirmed to Milo that age did not determine productivity.

Whatever the cause of Charles and Fred's slowness, it was clear that Esther and Alisha were carrying them. That Esther or Alisha had not yet yelled out, "light a fire under it" to Fred was a wonder to Milo. Knowing that the core measure was reasonable, knowing it was possible and knowing his artisans were fully aware of the subs per rush measure made Milo comfortable with the requirement.

Esther had convinced him that the highest performers should be rewarded. Did that mean then, that he endlessly weeded out the lowest performers in search of ever-faster sub artisans? If he had four sub artisans pumping out 80+ subs per rush, and one at 63, did he get rid of the low producer and bring in somebody new hoping they'd also be at the 80+ mark?

Could Milo enforce the core measure? Could he hold his artisan's accountable to the minimum standard of 60 subs per rush? Milo was satisfied that he could. Nothing in Dave's letter had cast doubt on the core measure. Dave's Subs would be served by holding his employees accountable to a minimum expectation, as long as they knew of the expectation, it was possible, and the expectation was reasonable.

On the other hand, Milo suspected there would be diminishing returns for always pursuing the fastest artisans. While the production disparities were obvious to everyone, Milo knew that Charles and Fred were well liked. If wasn't a question of Esther and Alisha wanting Charles and Fred gone and replaced by faster sub artisans. Esther, in particular, just wanted to be rewarded for being the fastest. "No," Milo thought. "Charles and Fred are good employees. My task is really to coach them to faster productivity."

HOME CONSTRUCTION

"Wait, wait," yelled Isabel as she turned her head toward the access road adjacent to the freeway. "Get off at this next exit. I see it!"

"See what?"

"The perfect present," she said.

Exhausted after fighting the holiday crowds and coming up empty handed on the girls' big present, Milo did as instructed and turned back, along the access road, to the place Isabel had seen.

It was an outdoor play equipment store. Actually a small shack, with multiple configurations of home playground equipment out front, all in deep brown wood, with green and yellow awnings above the raised floors.

"Sweetie, they already have a swing set," said Milo.

"It's not a swing set I pursue, my love," said Isabel in an upbeat tone. "Just pull in, toward the shack."

The gravel driveway led toward the shack, and as they got close Milo could finally see what Isabel had seen.

"That's it," she said, looking at the bright pink with white trim playhouse now directly in front of their car.

It was about eight feet wide, six feet deep and five feet tall. It had a little door and open framed windows on each side. It was constructed from wood, with a painted cedar exterior. It was gorgeous. It was perfect.

"This is it," said Isabel. That was all it took, an hour at the store and they had purchased the "big" present. It would be the grand finale of the holiday morning. The only problem was how to hide it.

"How do you hide a playhouse?" asked Isabel. "Actually, how to we even get it to our house?"

"It's a kit," said the salesman. "We'll deliver it to your house in brown boxes. Your girls won't know what it is."

"Do we have to build it?" asked Isabel, skeptically.

"Piece of cake," said the salesman. "It comes with very simple instructions."

"Yeah," said Milo. "Like he says, piece of cake. Of course I can put together a playhouse."

Milo and Isabel bought the playhouse, scheduling the delivery on a day the girls were in school. They had it all planned out. They would build the playhouse in the living room, the night before the holiday and there the playhouse could sit until the snow melted in the spring, a small sacrifice for the joy in their girls' faces Milo and Isabel agreed.

Six boxes arrived four days before the holiday. Milo hid them in his garage, under a blue tarp, away from the door to the house. Milo had already reached out to his brother-in-law, Benny. Isabel's sister Lauren and Benny would come for dinner and then Benny and Milo would build the playhouse, right there in the living room, after the girls went to bed.

Finally, about 10:00 pm, the two girls safely asleep, Benny and Milo brought the boxes into the living room. They were numbered, 1-6. Out came the wood, pre-painted pink and white pieces of cedar siding, Douglas fir frames, and six-ply plywood floor sections. About 100 pieces in all, although they didn't do the count. Pulled from the boxes, it was now a gigantic collection of wood. In addition to the wood, in box number 1 there were three heavily taped bags of metal supports, bolts, nuts, washers, and wood screws. Benny had torn open the bags and a pile of hardware now sat next to the pile of wood. They were ready, but they had no idea where to start.

"Where are the instructions?" asked Milo.

"I don't know," replied Benny.

"Isabel, did we get instructions when we bought the playhouse?" asked Milo.

"None that we got when we purchased." replied Isabel. "Aren't they in the box?"

"Not that we could find," replied Milo.

"Let's go," said Isabel turning to Lauren. "The boys need our help." Ten minutes into their collective search for the instructions, Isabel said, "Alright, I give up. I can't find the instructions either."

"That's OK. Milo and I can figure it out," said Benny trying to stay positive as the clock ticked out the minutes.

Milo was growing increasingly uneasy about the prospects of building the playhouse without instructions. And his instincts were right. Benny and he fumbled around for about an hour, laying out pieces of wood, laying hardware next to each, in hopes that they could match hardware with their associated wooden structural items.

At this point, Isabel and Lauren were sitting on the sofa, marveling at their progress – or lack thereof. "Are you sure you can do this without instructions?" they would alternate asking at roughly 10 minute intervals.

"I don't see any pieces of wood joined together," commented Isabel when the hands on the clock read midnight, sounding concerned. "You know that the girls will be awake in about seven hours?"

"We got this," said Benny, as if responding to a mediaeval challenge between rival knights.

"Perhaps I'd better look at their website?" said Isabel referring to the manufacturer of the playhouse.

"Maybe that would be a good idea," said a discouraged Milo.

It took Isabel less than 10 minutes to find, download and print the instructions. Thirty-two pages of step-by-step instructions. Each page had a wonderful illustration showing how to assemble the pieces, with a small table at the base of the page, showing which pieces of hardware would be used. The instructions were the key to the entire building project; by 12:15, the race to the finish had begun. Milo and Benny began to assemble the playhouse, this time with the invaluable assistance of the instructions.

The race against time ended about 3:30 in the morning. By that time, Benny and Lauren had decided to spend the night. In fact, seeing visual progress in the build, Lauren and Isabel had called it a night about at 2:00 a.m.

All four adults were sound asleep at 7:30 a.m., when they awoke to the joyful screaming of the two little girls as they ran into their parents' room, "You've got to see it," said Emily. It was a holiday to be cherished, everything that Milo and Isabel has hoped for.

228

The week before New Year's was slow at the store. The few business people working in the building during this week ate out less, bringing in leftovers or attending work parties serving holiday food. Although Milo was working, as were two artisans, Milo had a lot of time to think about Isabel and his two girls. Each night his girls had invited him for tea or dinner in the playhouse. It was cramped inside, the ceiling was low, but Milo could think of no better place to be.

Instructions made the difference between disaster and success for the mission. Milo and Benny needed someone to tell them *how* to assemble the playhouse. And that was the word running through his head. *How.*

"Cheese, meat, condiments, and veggies in that order." It had been around since Dave's Subs had opened six years ago. It was the most basic form of instruction. Not a 32-page set of instructions, just a simple one liner, taught to every new artisan: "Cheese, meat, condiments, and veggies in that order." At Dave's Subs, this was not merely instruction for laying sub ingredients; it was an expectation, a rule actually. Dave's Subs had played with the order of ingredients to determine which order made the most sense. Condiments on the bottom meant a soggy roll. Meat on the bottom meant the same. Cheese on the bottom provided a buffer between the roll and the topping that might soak into the bread. After much experimentation, Dave had set the order. The cheese goes on first, followed by the meat, followed by the condiments, and then the vegetables. Keep soggy stuff from the roll. That was the strategy.

Dave created instructions for his employees. When they were best practice, he made them the rule. Rules were different than instructions. Instructions were optional. Rules came with consequences for not following them. Cheese, meat, condiments, and veggies in that order, was a rule. Artisans were told how to assemble the sub. Build the subs Dave's way, or find another job. It was that simple.

Milo knew that even with a rule he should expect his artisans to make a mistake. "Cheese, meat, condiments, and veggies in that order." His employees could have the order in their brains each and every time they made a sandwich; yet, there remained that inescapable fallibility we all shared. The System 1 brain would make the order of ingredients a habit, a rule turned routine. That would allow an artisan's System 2 brain to focus on the customer. Errors were to be expected, but Milo knew they would be rare. One in a hundred, perhaps, or one in a thousand. Milo knew he could live with those odds.

The problem lay in the at-risk behaviors, Milo knew. "What do I do if artisans choose to deviate from the required order?" Milo asked himself. It was not an easy answer for him. An improperly sequenced placement of sub ingredients would harm no customers. Reckless didn't seem to fit.

It seemed certain, however, that his artisans might drift from the rule. That is, they would lose touch with the reason for the rule, and perhaps find it easier to sequence sandwiches in another way. After all, customers almost always order meat first, then cheese. Yet, to grab roast beef and put in on the bottom half of the roll meant a little roast beef oozing onto that bottom roll.

Milo knew he should expect his artisans to slowly drift away from the rule, but he also knew it was his job to keep it in view. To that end, he posted the order at each artisan's station, and audited it as he routinely observed his artisans' work. If he saw a pattern, he coached the employee at the end of her shift. It was not discipline; it was simply an opportunity to help his artisans maintain the order.

Milo believed it was his job as manager to coach and mentor his employees. If they were not responsive to that coaching, only then would he have a much more serious conversation. Only in that conversation did he discuss whether or not a particular artisan was willing to conform to the instruction turned rule.

"Cheese, meat, condiments, and veggies in that order." It was the rule. Milo did not expect perfection. He even expected some drift. In fact, he figured he'd have to speak to each of his employees about this specific rule at one time or another, possibly more than once depending on how long they remained with Dave's Subs.

In the end, though, it was up employees to choose to comply – or not. And then it was up to Milo to make decisions based on his employees' compliance. Did the rule violation stem from human error, was it at-risk, or was it reckless? For Milo, it was the nature of the violation that would be of most interest to him. The rules laid out the expectations, how to deal with any breach would be based upon his evolving model of human fallibility. Console the human error, coach the at-risk, and sanction the reckless.

WHY ALISHA?

"Fast and friendly service," that was the mantra. Subs per rush was the measure of speed, the measure of "fast." Milo was satisfied that he could measure employee performance by how fast they were pushing subs out the door.

Dave had a second core measure, and it was targeted at "friendly." Since his first store opened, Dave had tracked the rate at which customers returned to a particular artisan using a sophisticated software program that Larry's brother had created for Dave back in the day. If a customer really liked Dave's Subs, Dave estimated that they might eat there once or twice a month, or 10-20 times in a year.

Data was taken from credit and debit card transactions. The computer tracked each name, assigned it a random number, allowing Dave to track the artisan for each customer visit through his or her de-identified number. As a system it worked very well. If a customer showed up 10 times during the year, and if they spread their patronage among the five artisans, meaning two customer visits per artisan, the customer was logged as showing no preference. They were returning customers for the store, which was a good thing. That customer, however, spreading their business among the five artisans, did nothing to demonstrate loyalty to a particular artisan.

If the data showed a preference for one artisan, then that customer would be considered a repeat customer for that single artisan. To be seen as preferential, a customer would have to visit one artisan at double the rate of the next most used artisan. So, a customer who spread 10 visits among 5 artisans, yet visited one artisan 4 times, the others at 2, 2, 1 and 1, would be considered a repeat customer. It was an easy computer algorithm and it gave Dave his second measure.

It was a great measure for Dave's Subs. If an artisan were rude, a customer was not likely to return. If an artisan were unsanitary, the customer would not return. The pace at Dave's was very fast, yet Dave wanted his artisans to be so friendly that customers would go out of their way to see a particular artisan. Return rate was the measure for the "friendly" part of fast and friendly service.

Five months into his tenure at Store #6, Dave provided Milo with his numbers. Dave thought it would take time to develop repeat customers, so Dave withheld this data until the store had a bit of history in its market. The numbers, "preference numbers" they were called, were as follows: Alisha – 4.5%, Bryce – 1.3%, Charles – 2.2%, Esther – 4.1%, and Fred – 1.9%. These numbers meant that 4.5% of Alisha's customers were repeat customers who showed a preference for Alisha as their artisan.

So what did Milo make of these numbers? First, Milo was intrigued, to say the least, that Alisha's customers showed the greatest preference. She was the artisan who made the mistake with Patti Foster. Were customers superstitiously believing that Alisha was pre-disastered and so was probably the safest artisan in the store? Did they feel sorry for her and the abuse that had followed in the immediate aftermath of her mistake? Or had some of her customers already developed a loyalty to Alisha pre-Patti Foster and simply continued to come to her because they really liked her? Milo knew his question was probably unanswerable; he just had to accept that Alisha had the best preference numbers at this time.

Milo knew the numbers from Store #1. The repeat customer rate for the store, those returning within a year, was roughly 80%. Four out of five customers at Dave's Subs were repeat customers. For one out of five, it was a first-time visit to the store. Milo also knew that with stable artisans, all working at a very high level of speed, preference numbers grew to around 8-10%. That is, roughly one out of 10-12 customers showed a preference for a particular artisan.

Milo could see that his preference numbers tracked closely to an artisan's speed. That was to be expected in the busy downtown business lunch environment. If an artisan hustled, customers would notice, and make a point of coming back to that artisan. Speed was a very strong value for Dave's Sub's customers. Alisha and Esther were the highest producers, and thus, had the best preference numbers.

Bryce had the lowest numbers at 1.3 although he was not very far from Charles and Fred. The three guys were at the bottom of the scorecard. Milo knew that it wasn't a preference based on gender; male artisans at each of the other stores easily achieved preference numbers in the 8-10% range, again, seemingly based in part on their speed.

"The numbers are what they are," Dave had told Milo. "It's up to the artisan to get their numbers up. Fast and friendly service. Focus on fast and friendly service, and you will get to 75 subs in a rush, with 10% preference scores." Dave realized that there were people who couldn't do this; they were likely not the right people to work at Dave's Subs.

Now for Milo, it was a bit of a quandary to understand how he would hold his employees accountable to this second core measure. The first measure had an expectation – 60 subs per rush. To work at Dave's, an artisan needed to produce 60 subs per rush. It was a condition of employment. If an employee did not meet the expectation, their employment could be terminated.

The preference number was different. Employees were not told of this as an expectation. There was no minimum number that artisans had to meet. Artisans were tracked just the same, and they knew they were being tracked. Yet, there was no minimum expectation. Milo had his earlier criteria: his employees had to know, it had to be possible, and it had to be reasonable. But that was for expectations. There was no expectation here. No 5% minimum preference. There was only the tracking of data. Yet tracking of data that Dave himself thought to be the second most important measure of artisan success, second only to subs per rush.

Milo brought it to Dave's attention. "So why is it we don't have a minimum expectation for preference numbers?" asked Milo.

"Why would we?" Dave replied.

"Because if we are going to hold employees accountable for their preference number, shouldn't they know what that number is?" replied Milo.

Dave, being a big Yankees fan, asked, "Does a baseball player have a minimum batting average?"

"No, but that's sports," replied Milo.

"Yes, but it's a job as well," said Dave. "It's funny that sports teams don't set minimum expectations, yet the way we track stats sure puts an emphasis on those stats when it comes to their next contract."

"Yeah," said Milo, "It's clearly relevant."

"And for us, subs per rush and the preference number are our way of tracking the performance of an individual artisan," said Dave. "Just like store revenue and return customers are a means for tracking the performance of a store, and its manager."

Milo got the message. He could track data that told him how well an individual or his team was doing. Across society, we tracked data, from stock reports of corporations, to win/loss records of sports teams. Given the apparent imperative to measure, we tracked at the individual level as well. And those measures were relevant to an organization and employee's success, even if there was no stated minimum expectation.

Milo hadn't thought much about the return performance number until now. It was a measurement without end. What should Milo take from his numbers? Clearly, he should work to figure out why his guys were underperforming. Or why Alisha and Esther were performing so well. The mere fact that the artisan numbers were under 5% across the board meant Milo had work to do. Dave was tracking him. And Dave was expecting, if he could use that word, preference numbers in the 8-10% range across his five artisans. There was work to do.

Umbrellas Indeed

Milo was growing comfortable with rate-based outcomes. There was nothing unjust about having expectations, and it was reasonable to reward high performers. What was bothering Milo were those outcomes that stood alone as single outcomes, things that looked more project focused, like building a barn. These outcomes are not rate-based like subs per hour. The barn would be built only once. And the employee whose job it was to build it would be judged on that single barn. Thinking about this took Milo back to the Memorial Day weekend, a couple months after the Patti Foster event.

As they approached the Memorial Day weekend, Milo mentioned to his team that he wanted to take advantage of four new outdoor tables with umbrellas he was about to put outside the store. Milo was hoping that the outside tables might attract customers from neighboring buildings, but mentioned that he was running out of time to market this new summer time offering.

Esther, ever energetic, asked if she could get some extra hours taking on the marketing for Milo. It was a project task, with an objective and a completion date, all rolled up into one big deliverable. Esther could put together a plan, and execute the plan. And that's just what she did.

About two weeks before Memorial Day, Esther brought a flyer to Milo she had created using a free version of design software. Shaped like an outdoor table and umbrella, done in full color, it far exceeded what Milo had had in mind. Milo gave Esther the manager's name at the local print shop Dave's Subs used and told her that he would take care of the bill. She just needed to get 500 copies of the flyer printed, and then handed out to businesses in a two-block radius of the shop. Importantly, the flyers needed to be handed out between Wednesday and Friday of the week ahead of Memorial Day weekend, so that customers would see them in advance of the Memorial Day week, when the new tables would be set up.

Unfortunately, because of her own load studying for finals, Esther did not deliver some of the flyers until after the holiday weekend. Although disappointed at the late delivery, Milo considered the campaign a moderate success. He did talk with Esther about the late delivery, however.

"Esther, what happened with the delivery?" said Milo.

"Yeah, I'm sorry about that. I couldn't deliver them all before the holiday. Actually, I delivered about half of them after the holiday. I had finals the week before, and I just got bogged down in studying. My younger brother promised to help me, but he forgot he had this baseball camp over in Cooperstown. That really threw me off," said Esther. "I hate when people make promises and then don't deliver!"

"But, Esther, you could have given me a call. I would have helped hand them out. If it was going to slide, you needed to let me know," said Milo.

"Oh, I didn't even think about giving you a call," said Esther. "I'm really sorry."

"Esther, you did a great job on the flyers, but you needed to come to me for help on the delivery," Milo said, ending the conversation.

It was an outcome-based expectation. Esther volunteered to produce an outcome – a marketing campaign pulled off before Memorial Day weekend. It was not a rate-based outcome, but a project outcome – to be assessed as an individual outcome on its own. Milo used words like on schedule, and under budget when thinking about this project. There was no rate to track. Milo merely tracked completion. A project was either successful or it wasn't, and in this case, success looked like perfection. Esther, in taking on responsibility for this task, was still an inescapably fallible human being. She was bound to make mistakes *during* the process. Yet, with good planning, she should have had time to recover from mistakes, within her own process of producing the outcome.

Milo could see the difference quite clearly in his guitar studio. He'd ask his students to play at a recital. He hoped for close to perfection, but he could not expect it. Even the best were apt to make mistakes along the way. During the recital (but not during practice), his students moved on after a mistake. There was no starting over, or the recital would never end.

When a beginning student handed a guitar to Milo to tune, however, they expected Milo to return a tuned guitar. If Milo made a mistake in how far he turned a tuning peg on the head of the guitar, he kept adjusting until he had the right pitch. It was a process of trial and error, getting increasingly closer to a perfectly tuned guitar. He would never make one attempt, hear the pitch was off, but return it to the student, with a lame, "Sorry, I messed up."

Milo saw that project outcomes have a unique characteristic in that recovery is available within the creation of the outcome. There is no recovery in the song played at a recital. A student cannot un-ring that bell. Yet, the guitar tuner can keep getting it wrong until its right. Move the tuning peg, test, move the tuning peg again, test, until the guitar is in tune.

Milo understood that Esther got caught between school demands and work demands. Milo knew that school was important to Esther. Her job at Dave's was a part-time job, and Milo was happy to make accommodations for that fact. It probably wasn't the best idea to offer the task to Esther on his part. And it clearly wasn't a good choice on her part to push the delivery of some flyers until after the holiday weekend.

Milo was upset with Esther. When she saw that she was running out of time, she should have informed Milo. She committed to an outcome when she volunteered to take on the marketing project. She failed, in part, to produce that outcome. Milo knew he could and should judge that failure. In her performance review, the partially failed project would be part of Esther's body of work, just as her running into the street to give aid to the automobile accident victim, and as her 85 subs/rush would be. These would all help paint the picture of who Esther was to Dave's Subs.

Rate-based outcomes formed the core measure of how artisans were performing at Dave's Subs. Employers hire employees to *do* something, and generally that "doing something" can be evaluated in rate-based terms. The Memorial Day marketing campaign clearly pointed to another type of outcome, a project outcome. The project might be big like building a skyscraper or a dam, or much smaller, like writing a report or managing a weekend marketing campaign.

While Dave's Subs did not lend itself to many discrete projects for artisans – after all, if artisans were busy working on projects they were likely *not* making subs. But Milo knew that he had already had several projects since Store #6 had opened that would figure in the upcoming performance evaluations. Off the top of his head, he could easily come up with three: the near miss at the park dedication with the overheated subs, Charles and Bryce's website project and now the Memorial Day weekend marketing campaign. In addition to the core measures, each of these contributed to his artisans' total body of work at Dave's Subs.

Culture or Bust

After the holidays, Milo spoke with his old friend, Lou Garuda. Lou was a career Navy man, having spent most of his sea time on aircraft carriers. Milo told Lou about the Patti Foster event, and about his journey trying to figure out the human beings he had working for him. Lou was just the guy for Milo. He was a Chief Petty Officer, which meant he had his own team to supervise. Milo wanted to know more about what was helpful to a strong work culture. And from what he knew from Lou, the flight deck of an aircraft was the place to find one.

"Interesting stuff you've had to deal with, Milo," said Lou. "I'm particularly intrigued by this idea of a 'risk monitor.'"

"Yeah, what about it intrigues you?" said Milo.

Well, when I was a young ensign, I was scared to death of the flight deck of an aircraft carrier," said Lou. "The noise, the danger – it was sheer terror. As a young ensign, I did what I was told. If there was a rule, I'd follow it. Now, that risk monitor you're talking about – it was on overload my first few days on the flight deck. To stay safe, I just did what I was told. I was told the rules, and I followed them. I guess that was my risk monitor working. I was too scared to even think about deviating from a rule given to me. I didn't know enough to deviate. Just following orders."

"So, you're a guy that follows the rules," said Milo. "You know that not everyone colors within the lines like you."

"No, no," said Lou. "You're missing where I'm heading. Now with 15 years in the Navy, I'm a slightly different guy. My risk monitor doesn't go off like it used to. It's much more subtle. And frankly, I don't comply with rules like I used to. I mean, I know more about the hazards around me. I can be smarter in my decisions, which means that I sometimes deviate when I see that to shortcut the rules will get me where I want to go."

"Getting a little loose in your old age?"

"Thirty four years old is not old, unless you're comparing me to a 10 year old," said Lou. "But 15 years into my work life, my perspective has changed. And I gotta tell you what I see. The younger sailors make more mistakes than us old farts, if you want to call me that. But, what I see, at least anecdotally, is that the older sailors deviate more from the rules. It's like we're hazards at both ends of the spectrum. More errors early on, more choices to deviate from rules later on."

"You know, Lou, that actually makes sense. The less you know, the more you stick with the safety of the rules provided around you," said Milo. "The more you think you know, the more situational life becomes. I actually see it in my twins. At six, they see life in black and white terms. If I ever get caught in the gray space of life, I just ask a six year old what they think is right. It's incredible what insight they have. We're trying to rationalize away our poor choices, while the twins see them for what they are. It's weird."

"Yeah, it seems the more we've been around, in some ways, the bigger the risk we become. My sister is a nurse. She says at her hospital they never let an experienced nurse, say a 20 year nurse, train the new nurses," said Lou.

"Wait, why is that?" said Milo.

"She said it's because they don't know what to teach. By the time they have been working somewhere for 20 years, what they teach is how they do it, and after 20 years, that's often different than the rulebook. So, they use newer nurses, ones that have been around 2-3 years," said Lou.

Milo's been thinking about that risk monitor again. How can he help his artisan's risk monitors not fall prey to the enticing lure of drift? Rules help; they point employees in the right direction. But as time goes on, employees start to drift. And when they drift, their risk monitors are not firing. Lou spoke of how his team drifted away from the rules as they grew more skilled at what they did. Milo saw it as a bit of a double-edged sword. He wanted his artisans to be skilled, *and* to follow the rules. He wanted both.

Milo had heard the term "safety culture" used before, but he really didn't know what that meant, at least operationally. But he was beginning to understand. Milo could design a great system and expect his artisans to perform safely and according to the rules within that system. He wasn't talking about human error, nor really about the reckless choice. To Milo, at-risk behavior was his biggest safety risk. It was the measure of his culture. A strong safety culture meant that employees would make safe choices. And that, at least in part, meant that their risk monitors were working well. They could be compliant with procedures, but above and beyond that, they needed to steer away from risky choices.

To combat that drift into at-risk behavior, Milo thought he had to help each artisan train his or her own risk monitors. Milo didn't think that the problem was his artisans' System 2 brains disregarding the input from their risk monitors; rather, their risk monitors were not going off. Wild Bill had it pegged. That out-loud, gluten-free safety check was ripe for at-risk behavior. The lunch rush is on, production is the mission, and it's sometimes hard to be respectful of values along the way. The risk monitor becomes key. And Milo needed a way to help his artisans train their risk monitors. How could his artisans be fast, be experienced, and yet have fully active, well-tuned risk monitors?

Milo knew that the memory of the Patti Foster event would keep his artisans on a safe path as it related to gluten free bread - at least for now, while the memory of the event was still fresh in everyone's minds and there were no new employees who hadn't personally experienced the justifiable wrath of Patti Foster. Heck, a customer could hardly order gluten-free without bells and whistles going off. Everyone took notice, customers and artisans alike.

Butt, that was for gluten-free bread. That didn't necessarily mean that the artisans would de-glove and re-glove when they were supposed to. For that risk, touching something gross, and then touching food, there was no recent memory causing each artisan's risk monitor to fire.

Milo could spot the problem with at-risk behavior. Now, however, he had a measure of store culture; he just didn't have the answer for reducing it. Milo was consoled by the knowledge that at-risk behavior was universal. Wild Bill could spot it, and Lou could spot it. The bigger problem was fixing that culture when it began to drift. Milo knew, the more at-risk behavior, the worse his culture.

Showing Off

It was the week between Christmas and New Year's, time for the annual managers' lunch. Dave always hosted a picnic in the spring for employees and their families, but this was only for his store managers in appreciation for their hard work over the year. It was time to reflect on the year that had passed, and a time to look forward to the year to come. Given the stores were slow during the week between Christmas and New Year's anyway, it made it easy for the managers to skip out for a while.

This was Milo's first time at the managers' lunch. Dave was always sure to choose a nice restaurant; this year's choice was a fine steakhouse, packed in the evenings, only slightly less crowded at lunchtime with good food, good waiters, and a good professional lunch atmosphere. Dave required business professional attire; it was a business meeting, and Dave wanted some formality mixed in with the pleasure of bringing the store managers together.

Their waiter was a young man, probably in his late 20's, wearing black pants and a tuxedo shirt with a black bow tie. This was a formal place, designed to impress. After ordering drinks, the managers ordered their lunches. There were seven at the table, Dave's six managers and Dave himself. The ordering started with Dave, who was closest to the waiter when he approached the table.

A salad to start, a cut of prime steak, and a side or two. The steak would be cooked just as they liked it, with a choice of optional sauces that were the specialty of the house: crumbled bleu cheese, cracked peppercorn, mesquite fired, a red wine reduction, or simply plain. Mouths were already watering.

As the waiter took orders, one by one, the managers quickly noticed that the waiter was not writing anything down. Most were comfortable with the idea of memorizing one or two people's orders, but seven?

"Aren't you going to write this down?" asked Milo.

"Not my style," said the waiter.

"I sure hope your memory serves you," said Dave, remembering his terrible experience at the racetrack.

The waiter completed the order, and then, of interest now to the entire team, repeated it back, pointing a finger at each person as he repeated their order.

Kyle, one of the other store managers, said "Impressive, impressive indeed."

Dave and Milo just looked at each other, as if they were in on a joke of which no one else was aware. This lunch was becoming a laboratory experiment of sorts, much of their discussions on system design, employee reliability and behavior coming together in one managers' lunch.

Unfortunately, Dave, Milo and the rest of Dave's managers were lab rats as well in this waiter's own recall experiment. It remained to be seen how the strategy of memorizing the orders would turn out. The waiter's verbal recall was a good strategy for catching mistakes before they made it to the kitchen. So far, he'd made no mistakes. That said, it seemed unnecessarily risky to both

Dave and Milo. After all, they weren't at this well-known steakhouse because it was known for its waiters' memories.

The salads came out first. All as ordered. So far, so good.

The steaks and sides came out next, in the hands of three food runners. There weren't any obvious preparation issues, the steaks all appeared to be cooked as ordered, and none of the managers was complaining. It was the sauces where the problem occurred. Kyle's steak was missing the cracked peppercorn, and Robin's had a mass of crumbled bleu cheese on top when she had ordered the red wine reduction. Kyle's was easily fixed, but Robin's steak needed to be recooked, leaving her to watch as the rest of the table dug in to their lunches.

Milo and Dave looked across the table at each other. It was too much to stay silent. They had to talk about it with the rest of the managers. Most of the managers were kind enough to give the poor waiter some grace, commenting how difficult it was to memorize seven people's orders and that the waiter had actually done a reasonable job given the difficulty. Dave, Milo, and Robin were a little less forgiving.

"Milo, so do you want to tell your fellow managers what just happened?" said Dave.

"Sure," Milo swallowed his bite of food.

"Since the Patti Foster event last April, Milo has been exploring the concepts of workplace accountability," said Dave. "His investigation really began with that letter we gave to all employees, including each of you at this table, committing to not firing them for making a mistake. He's been making some really good progress, but has really opened up a can of worms across a bunch of different areas of accountability. Two big things he's looked at are system design and employee choices within those systems. So, what do you notice about this waiter's system, Milo?"

"Well, I think our waiter was gambling with our order. To show off to us, something I don't appreciate as much as he does, he decided to memorize our orders. I bet Robin's not too impressed either! Memorizing our order was an at-risk behavior," said Milo.

"A what?" said Robin, having nothing to do but engage the conversation given her steak was still on the grill.

"An at-risk behavior," said Milo. "It's a risky choice where, in this case an employee, did not appreciate the risk he was taking. Our waiter was taking risks with our orders. His decision to memorize our orders increased the chances that he would make a mistake. And for you, Robin, that's exactly what happened."

"So, Milo, what would you do with this waiter?" asked Dave.

"First, I'd ask the manager whether memorizing an order was part of the restaurant's system design. That is, did the restaurant instruct its waiters to memorize orders? Was this a job requirement?" said Milo.

"And where would that lead you?" asked another manager.

"If it was organizationally endorsed, I would quit coming back to this restaurant. The organization owns it," said Milo. "If the organization made it clear that memorizing orders was not a good practice, then I would start talking to other waiters. What was their practice? What did they think of memorizing orders?"

"Would you ever consider talking to this waiter?" one of his fellow managers asked with more than a hint of sarcasm.

"Yes," answered Milo. "Of course, I would talk to this waiter. But I'd gather some information first. I'd want to know what this waiter was thinking. Did he believe he was in a safe place memorizing orders? If he did, I'd coach him. That is, I'd let him know that memorizing orders was not good practice. The risks of a messed up order outweighed the showmanship value of memorizing orders."

"And you think that would solve the problem?" asked another manager.

"Yes, I do," said Milo. "But if it didn't, if the waiter was not responsive to coaching, then I would move him on."

"You'd fire him?" asked Dave.

"I would, indeed," Milo replied firmly.

"Is that consistent with what we committed to do after your gluten-free event?" asked Robin.

"Yes, I believe it is completely compatible with our commitment," said Milo. "We committed to not firing an employee simply because they made a mistake. Yes, our waiter messed up our orders – and there were undoubtedly memory errors involved. But that's not why I would fire him. Our waiter apparently sees value in memorizing his orders. Perhaps he found that he gets tipped better when he shows off. His interest aside, if memorizing orders is not a requirement, then I think this waiter should be writing them down – because this is in my, the customer – interest. That's what his manager should be coaching him around. And if he chooses to memorize orders after being told not to, then it's time for that waiter to move on. At that point, I'd fire him."

"Wow," said another of the managers.

"Totally," said Dave. "Milo, that was great! Now guys, Robin's steak is finally here. Let's forget about our waiter and dig in."

Milo felt like he scored a run at lunch. After Robin, he was the new kid on the block, and he'd held his own in the discussion about the waiter. And, to his immense satisfaction, his argument met no resistance. Milo could tell he was onto something, a model of workplace accountability that made sense intuitively and that worked.

Milo went home that evening thinking a lot about his lunch. To hold his own was important to him. Yet, most of his System 2 thinking had moved past the discussion at lunch. The waiter was a blessing, Milo could see. He allowed Milo to look more closely at the relationship between choices and errors. The waiter was making mistakes with the orders. That word, mistake, is what every customer would use. Yet, Milo could see that the more important aspect of the event was the precursor choice that the waiter was making. It was his choice to memorize orders that increased the likelihood of the ordering errors. And that was what was most important to Milo.

Milo could imagine, over the course of this waiter's short career at this restaurant, that his customers were riddled with his ordering errors. Perhaps the waiter could get it right with two, three, or even four customers. But five, six, seven, or eight would be more problematic. And the manager, they might only get notice of the results. A customer here, a customer there – all saying that their order was messed up. It would take a more sophisticated customer to expose the underlying at-risk behavior, and to inform the manager of the behavior.

THE BODY OF WORK

Milo did not originally plan a second report to Dave. Yet, Esther's frustration led Milo to push beyond the single event, into the body of work. It was round two for Milo, both in his concept development and in his report out to Dave.

"You know I've been practicing," Dave began.

"Practicing what?" asked Milo.

"Your model. I wrote it down on a post-it, put it in my wallet. Here it is. Console the error, coach the at-risk, sanction the reckless, all independent of outcome," said Dave.

"That's awesome. Not that you want to always be judging other people, of course. But if you find yourself in that position, then you have a good roadmap," said Milo.

"Yeah, it worked. Made it clear for me. But I have to tell you, there is an awful lot of at-risk behavior in the world. I thought I was going to see more errors, but that wasn't the case. Sure, out on the road I saw a few red lights run, might have been mistakes. But, geez, the things people do when they drive - if you look, I'd be surprised if *any* of their brain is on driving," said Dave.

"That's their System 1 doing the heavy lifting for them," said Milo.

"I saw this guy driving a huge SUV, holding onto his phone, his other hand flailing around like he was speaking to somebody right there in front of him, all animated, and he was just tooling down the road. He was either in an argument, or describing some horrific accident he'd seen - you could just see it in his face. Totally fixated on his conversation. And, I was convinced - his risk monitor was not firing at all. I don't think it could have gotten a word in edge wise. Amazing," said Dave.

"And there you were, driving to work, fixated on the guy in the car next to you?" teased Milo.

"Yes, I was. You were the one who told me to be watching," responded Dave. "Lucky I had my System 1 brain to get me to work. Anyway, I think I got the three behaviors down. It did leave me with one question, though. What am I to do with a person who is not responsive to coaching? I mean, I could have spoken to that guy about toning down the distractions when driving, but I am guessing he wouldn't have been responsive, kind of like your woman eating cereal," said Dave.

"We coach people because we know they are apt to drift. In some cases, we cause them to drift. In some cases, it's just us trying to save a bit of time, like that guy trying to drive and talk to a friend at the same time. But we human beings have some obligation to listen when we're coached. Just like the police officer a few months ago who told you to slow down. If we don't listen, we ultimately face sanction. Not so much for the at-risk behavior itself, but for our failure to respond to coaching. Get too many speeding tickets, ultimately your license gets taken. An employee who does not respond to coaching ultimately faces sanction, which may include losing his job if the sanction doesn't work. So, long story, but there is a path for the person who's not responsive," said Milo.

"Well, that seems reasonable. I knew you'd probably thought about that. Ok, so what's next in my education?" asked Dave.

"Hardly an education, Dave," said Milo.

"No, I really mean that. You're giving me an education I somehow missed. I didn't get to think about these issues as a trader. This stuff certainly wasn't included in my 'How to Start a Small Business' course. Really. Seems weird when I think about it. Maybe they thought every business owner just had to figure this stuff out on their own? But you're demonstrating that there's actually some logic to this, that there are words to articulate what it means to be a great manager, ways to design the employment environment and policies for managing that work for everybody," said Dave.

"Wow…that's humbling. Thank you, Dave," Milo said quietly. And then with a twinkle in his eyes, he said, "But you know there's more," Milo smiled. "We need to sort through the body of work. Well, multiple bodies of work. I'm coming up on performance appraisals. Having been on the receiving end as one of your employees for a few years, and on the receiving end of Esther's significant displeasure with my first efforts, I'd like to add a bit to our process," said Milo.

"What do we need to add?"

"Hang in there. I'm not asking for more money! Here's what I've been thinking about. Every person comes to work to get something out of work. My attorney friend, Ellen, calls this a "bargained for exchange." The employer gets work; the employee gets paid. Very simple equation. Employees work for a variety of reasons. In some cases, like for Charles, there are intangibles like getting out of the house, feeling productive, interacting with other humans. For Alisha there is the work that will ultimately lead her to be a restaurant owner herself.

"As we both now are intimately aware, however, employees come to us as inescapably fallible humans beings with the additional curse or blessing, depending on your perspective, of free will. They also come with individual talents, developed, perhaps, over years of hard work. We as the employer get to judge that talent. We also get to judge their choices. So here it is in a nutshell, an equation of sorts. Talent plus choices plus luck equals outcomes. Three components to look at the outcomes our employees produce," said Milo.

"Ok, tell me how this works with our core measure?" asked Dave.

"Right! We set an expectation of 60 subs per rush. That's what we expect our artisans to produce, with the talent they bring to Dave's Subs, and with the choices they make while they're here. There is a bit of luck involved. Cranky customers slow them down, they may have off days, but as a whole, over time, luck should statistically work its way out of the equation. What I'm saying is that each artisan should be evaluated based upon what they bring to the table - the core measure is just that, core. It best represents the reason we hire artisans - to produce subs. The more subs an artisan makes – until he starts making more mistakes or getting snappy with customers - the better. So there is nothing inconsistent with our core measure. It works," said Milo.

"Good," said Dave. "So what about that second core measure, return customers?"

"It, too, is a reasonable proxy, for lack of a better word, for how our artisans are taking care of their customers. The better they apply their talent, the better choices they make, the more return customers," said Milo.

"And those two measures, that's the bulk of our performance appraisal," said Dave.

"Yeah, it is, I guess. But what about the intangibles?" asked Milo.

"Intangibles?"

"Intangibles like Charles and Bryce building that website for you, or Charles helping me mentor the younger artisans? Among my team, he's got the most intangibles. He's slow, but he has intangibles," said Milo. "To really be just in our evaluations, I think we need to consider the intangibles that an employee brings to Dave's Subs.

"Yeah, in football, that would be the older back-up quarterback. Filled with intangibles, just not the guy you want in the game if you want to win," cracked Dave.

"Right, but this isn't football. Life's full of people with different talents, and we should be evaluating all they bring to the table, not solely the core measures. Don't get me wrong. If Charles can juggle, or is great at solving puzzles, but can't make subs, that doesn't help us much. But his mentoring, as a fellow artisan, it's important and helpful," said Milo.

"All right, what now?" asked Dave.

"I need to talk to you about how we bring in all the events that occur during the year, including big events like Alisha's that started us down this road and all our team's events, those things that happen in a moment in time, from Fred's skateboarding accident to the foul-up with the mobile kitchen, to the Patti Foster event. They are all part of our body of work. They don't go away.

"Your letter didn't make them go away. And they mean something. My letting Fred skateboard across the store says something about me. Now, we just have to be better at understanding what those things mean, particularly when we get to the point of a more holistic performance appraisal. What influences the individual merit-raises you want for your team?" asked Milo.

"A rhetorical question I presume. I take it you have an answer?" asked Dave.

"Of course, and it starts with you and our customers. You've quite clearly articulated our core measures. It's in your motto, 'Good food, fast and friendly service.' These are our aspirations. Beyond our aspirations, is a set of values that we need to articulate. They come from a number of places - from you as our leader, from our customers, from our team, from our community. We begin with safe food, and a safe workplace for our employees. We add in a tolerant, respectful workplace, where we don't exhibit prejudice toward our fellow human beings, fiscal and environmental responsibility...there are a number of values we share as a community.

"We judge how our artisans align their conduct, specifically their choices, with Dave's Subs values. Are our artisans doing their work in a safe way? Are they respectful of our customers? Of each other? Most of the things we called 'events' in this last year were things that seem to breach the duty we owed toward our values. And within those events, we saw human errors, at-risk behaviors, and reckless choices. We dealt with them in the moment, yet they don't go away. They remain part of the artisan's body of work," finished Milo.

Dave looked at him thoughtfully. "You know, Milo, I was a basketball player back in high school. I think I was a junior when the University of Michigan Fab Five was playing. These five freshmen were five of the best players, as a team, to ever take the court. Chris Webber was the best of them. He grew up in Detroit. A national high school basketball player of the year. Anyway, the Fab Five made it to the NCAA championship game against North Carolina. If you love basketball, you already know this story."

Milo shook his head.

"You don't?" Dave asked incredulously. "Well, Michigan, was down by two points with 11 seconds left. Chris Webber was bringing up the ball toward mid-court in an attempt to tie the game. Two players had him trapped at mid-court, and in the excitement, under the pressure of the game, he called a time out. He wanted his team to regroup, to set up one final play to tie the game and take it into overtime. But get this, there were no timeouts left! He called a timeout when the University of Michigan was out of timeouts. It was a technical foul – sort of sealed Michigan's loss. I mean massive failure on Chris Webber's part. Twenty years later, basketball aficionados still talk about that time out," said Dave.

"So what happened to the guy?" asked Milo.

"He was the #1 pick in the NBA draft, as a sophomore. Incredible. He made like over 100 million dollars as an NBA player. Yet, that one human mistake, no one has forgotten it. As you said, it's part of his body of work. It never goes away," said Dave.

"Great story. But clearly, the guy overcame that pretty horrific mistake if he was the NBA #1 recruit?" said Milo.

"Well, kind of," replied Dave. "He was later indicted for taking payments from a booster in the Detroit area. I think he'd been accepting cash since he was in junior high. Pretty big scandal. The Fab Five had their tournament wins removed. But good point. The timeout error was nothing, remembered, but taken in the context of Chris Webber's entire basketball performance. In that context, it didn't mean much given he wasn't calling bad timeouts his entire career. Yet his choice to accept cash, in clear violation of the rules, that was bad stuff. And those choices did more to define him perhaps than his illustrious basketball career."

"Sounds like Lance Armstrong. Look as his body of work - seven Tour De France wins, a hero, until we discover he was doping all along," said Milo.

"Yeah, now the doping defines him. But then again, those seem to be beyond your definition of reckless choices. Those came with the deliberate intention to defraud us all. Anyway, I think I get it. The body of work matters. And you've got a strategy for how to evaluate it in the performance appraisal process?" asked Dave.

"Yes, I do," responded Milo. "We look at each employee's core production. That work which supports our mission. That's the centerpiece of their evaluation. Can they produce at the rate we've hired them to? Then, we look at how they respect our shared values along the way, and in doing that we look principally at their choices. Do their choices align with our values? It's the totality of their work that we judge. And it's what they expect us to judge."

"Seems sort of like what we do today, does it not?" asked Dave.

"Don't forget from where we've come. Alisha's error would have defined her - actually would have gotten her fired. Her mistake, her at-risk behavior, and of course the dreadful outcome, those would have been her body of work," said Milo.

"Point taken. I'll be interested to see the evaluations of your artisans. And, I'm sure, you'll be interested to see my evaluation of you," said Dave.

"As you always say, indeed," said Milo.

La Grande Jatte

It was a to be a grand day in the park. Spring was in the air, and Isabel wanted to take advantage of it. She'd gathered the twins and Milo in the car to head out toward Manhattan's Central Park. It was a 45-minute drive on a good day, perhaps 90 minutes on a day filled with traffic. Central Park was not their closest park, but The Metropolitan Museum of Art (or The Met as it's known to New Yorkers) was located on the park's east side. Isabel had packed lunch and a blanket so that they could eat in the park. And after some playtime in the park, they would head into the museum.

For Isabel, it was not an ordinary visit to The Met. This one was going to be special for Isabel, as she'd always been a fan of post-impressionist painting, particularly that of Georges Seurat. Like the more famous Vincent Van Gogh, Seurat was in a group of European painters who were breaking the mold from the popular impressionistic artists of the 1880s. Befitting Isabel's trip into the city, Seurat's most famous painting was entitled *Sunday Afternoon on the Island of La Grande Jatte.* Isabel had discovered that it would be on loan from the Art Institute of Chicago for a limited time at the Met.

Milo had artistic roots, with interests in music and the more visual arts. In fact, Isabel and Milo met in an art class in college. An appreciation for art was but one interest that bound them together. And it was their mission to make sure their twins appreciated art as well. So, after the very enjoyable picnic on that slightly brisk April day, they headed into the Met, and right toward the post-impressionist exhibit.

It was as if both Milo and Isabel were searching the crowd for a long lost friend. Any painting that was not *Sunday in the Park*, they ignored, at least for the moment. *Sunday in the Park* was their first stop.

"There it is," said Milo. He picked up the twins, one in each arm, so as to see over the large crowd gathered in front of the painting, probably five people deep at angle from the painting. They waited their turn to get close, less than five feet away at their closest, the painting itself behind ropes, with a Met guard standing on either side.

As they approached the painting, Emily blurted out, "Daddy, it's just a bunch of dots!"

"Yes, Emily, it is," said Milo.

"Sweetie, that's what makes is so famous," added Isabel.

"This guy's famous because he painted in dots?" added Sara. "Our teacher tells us not to do that."

"Yeah, maybe this painter needs to talk to Mrs. Chang," said Sara.

"The impressionists used nice, long strokes," said Isabel. "Seurat, the artist who painted this, was a 'neo-impressionist', because he broke with tradition and started painting with dots."

"And we drove from New Jersey to see this guy?" said the unabashed Emily.

"Yes, Emily, we did," said Isabel. "Seurat was ridiculed when he painted this. His fellow painters thought he was a quack, not a real artist. But he was being himself, making his own way. And he helped spawn a new style of painting."

Milo lay there on the blanket, on the little hill just north of the sailboat pond in Central Park. They weren't full size sailboats – the pond was too small for that - but remote control ones available for rent from the park. Three feet long, with all white hulls and white sails – probably 30 boats on the water. A beautiful site for Emily and Sara, who Milo caught glimpses of as they walked around the pond with their mother. Milo stayed on the blanket, laying flat on his back, looking up through the trees, his mind mulling over Emily's comment. "Daddy, it's just a bunch of dots," Emily had said when she'd gotten close to the Seurat painting.

Milo was amazed at the profundity of Emily's words. Ever since the Patti Foster event, Milo's mind had been focused on events; that is, until Esther raised the issue of equity among the raises. As a manager, Milo knew he needed to know how to respond to single events, and he was learning to do that. And he also knew that he needed to know how to look at a body of work. George Bailey, in *It's a Wonderful Life*, had an amazing body of work. But he also had the big event, or at least knew that he would be the one held responsible for it, the loss of $8000 dollars.

Emily's statement got him thinking in a direction he really did not want to go. Perhaps Emily was right. Perhaps life was just a collection of dots. Move away from the painting and you see a wonderful scene of families along the Seine River in France, watching, as were Milo's girls, toy boats afloat on the pond. It was in itself surreal, given the similarities between the painting and what they were experiencing at the moment. Knowing Isabel's knack for making the connection between art and real life, he had no doubt that she had precisely planned this experience.

Move in close to the painting of any neo-impressionist painter painting in what's now called "pointillism" and what we see is "a bunch of dots" to borrow from Emily. It was only when viewed from a distance, that the dots blended into the whole scene along the Seine.

Seurat's *Sunday in the Park at on the Island of La Grande Jatte* measured a full 7 by 10 feet. It was a huge painting, made up only of dots, but Milo thought it was a pretty great metaphor for life. Life was just a collection of dots – discrete events, discrete individuals who we were tasked to make sense of and live with.

Milo was thinking about those he knew, both acquaintances and friends. He was working through each of them – asking one question. Were they nice people? That's all he would allow his System 2 brain to focus on – were they nice? His brother in law, Benny – was he a nice person?

It was a seemingly easy question. If asked in casual conversation, he'd probably answer "yes," in very short order, remembering, perhaps, Benny's assistance on the girls' playhouse. Milo knew that response came from his System 1 brain. It's not like his System 2 brain had any real time to process the question, to ponder his answer, before his mouth uttered the words, "Yeah, he's nice." Ask him about his Aunt Maria, however, and he'd be quick to say "no," because whenever he thinks of Aunt Maria, he remembers Aunt Maria babysitting him and his sibs. She yelled at them all the time about, seemingly, everything. Milo did not think that Aunt Maria was nice at all, and he could quickly see that his impression was shaped by the years of Aunt Maria yelling at him.

Milo was beginning to believe that we all saw each other through a series of events, a series of dots. If Milo could remember a series of pleasurable dots, those that somehow reflected on the value of being nice, then he'd say that person was nice. If his memory recalled one or more negative dots, again those that reflected on the value of niceness, he'd probably say the person was not nice. If Milo had no recollection, his mind seemed to give the person the benefit of the doubt, a guarded – "Well, I guess she's nice."

Niceness was an abstract idea. Being overly nice, being not nice enough, those were hard things to specify. We knew it when we saw it. But it was events that formed the basis of our opinions. The dots were the body of work. We humans didn't really have another means to create a picture of another person other than by doing it through a series of dots. This was Milo's epiphany. We might not always be able to directly lay out a person's body of work. Just as Seurat's dots very clearly created an intimate portrait of a lovely Sunday at a park along a river when they were viewed from a distance and as a whole, our brains appeared able to form a judgment about an individual, out the dots, the events that created their body of work.

Many looked at the dot of Alisha's error, and by extension at Milo's store, and painted them as unsafe. Feed a gluten-filled roll to someone who asked for, and needed, one that was gluten-free, and you are "unsafe." That single dot could follow a person, or the store, around for some time. It certainly left an impression. That seemed reasonable for Milo. What didn't seem reasonable was to believe the dot was the entire picture. To see the body of work in any kind of reasonable way, a person, or in this case a manager, had to see the events, the dots, in their entirety. As goes the dots, so goes the view of the picture.

Seurat's painting was just playing tricks with Milo's eyes. Back away from the painting and Milo saw the park scene. Get close and he, like Emily saw little more than dots. When it comes to seeing events, we very quickly extrapolate to a bigger picture. Lance Armstrong was a great guy, until we knew he was doping. Hear of the doping, form an impression. Impressions get formed, one event at a time.

Milo thought about the looming performance evaluations. He already knew that the concept of a "body of work" would be integral to his judgment of employee performance. Today's excursion brought him to the conclusion that he could not directly see a body of work unless he assembled it as a collection of dots. Just asking, "is Charles a good employee?" took him down the path of thinking in dots. What had Charles done that put him in a positive light? What has Charles done that puts him in a negative light? Through a series of events, and collections of events, like subs per rush, Milo could paint a picture of each artisan. And it would be through that view, but stepping back from the individual dots, where he'd get the clearest sense of the picture each employee's body of work painted.

Milo had been beating himself up, concerned that he'd been so focused on single events that he'd missed the big picture. Esther pointed out that the big rock in the jar was production. And she was right, no matter how far back you moved to see the picture as a whole, right there as the central theme of the picture was Dave's core measure - the subs per rush minimum.

MAKING CHOICES

Milo had been working for nearly a year to make sense of Dave's letter and to make sense of his own views regarding employee accountability. Throughout the year, his brain had been occupied with single events. In those single events, Milo found human errors, at-risk behaviors, and the occasional reckless choice, such as Fred's choice to write "wow" on a customer's receipt. Yet all of it was in the context of events.

While he thought he was on track learning to be a manager as Dave had asked him, one of his highest performers felt he had lost focus on the big rock in the jar. Yes, the events along the way were important, but it was production that was king, however it was measured. If he was thinking about evaluating employee performance, he had to be thinking foremost about production. The peanut butter spread of raises, everyone rewarded the same, seemed as unjust to Esther as Patti Foster's calling for Alisha's termination appeared to Dave and him.

Accepting that humans would not be perfect did not mean we couldn't differentiate ourselves. Esther clearly thought that every individual was blessed with talents, some with more and some with less. Some of those talents would be used at work, some outside. The energy expelled at work was a choice on the part of each employee. Esther's very high rate of subs per rush was tied to the energy she brought to work and her choice to put her energy into her work. Esther believed she should be compensated for what she brought to Dave's Subs as Esther, the individual. That peanut butter spread from the last go-around did not.

Milo thought that Esther was right, and so did Dave. The peanut butter spread had to go. This next set of performance evaluations would have to be different. Milo had been gathering information around his five sub artisans for the past year. For this round of evaluations, he'd begin with the core measures, both subs per rush and rate of return customer. Then he'd search for other outcomes, rate-based and project based, like Esther's marketing project or Bryce and Charles's website creation. Then, he'd download his event database, largely from his own head.

What was each of his artisans involved in over the past year? It seemed odd that he would keep a record of wrongs, but that's exactly what he did. For Milo, it was just part of being human. Milo also kept a record of "rights," the times where his artisans went above and beyond what was required. Milo was simply trying to collect dots, as he assessed each artisan's body of work.

He didn't have the luxury of stats like a pro football team, where an extensive list of outcome data told the coach just where each player stood in relationship to the team. Milo needed a system. For now, a simple spreadsheet and what was in his head would have to do.

Milo first pulled the data on the core measures. Good data. Each artisan had improved his or her rate of subs per rush since the first evaluation six months earlier. Looking at the stats, Milo saw that Esther and Alisha were still the rock stars, Esther pumping out 88 subs per rush, and Alisha close behind at 86. Bryce was a distant second with a still respectable 77 subs per rush. Charles had hit – and maintained - just over the minimum at 63, while Fred hadn't moved off 62.

Milo was completely satisfied that subs per rush was the best single measure of his artisans' performance, given no egregious, reckless behavior that might overshadow this core measure. Milo was happy to be able to tell each artisan that they were meeting the minimum expectation of 60 subs per rush. He would also tell each artisan that he had an aspirational goal for the artisans at his store - it was possible, Milo knew, for artisans to get close to 90 subs per rush.

Milo knew he had to temper his language here, as he didn't want his team to sacrifice safety or hygiene safeguards, or rush so fast that they offended customers. But that didn't seem to be the case for Esther and Alisha, who were cranking out subs while also getting great customer reviews.

Milo looked next at the return customer data. This was an important measure for Dave. Dave felt that it was really his overall "quality" measure. If artisans were in any way not meeting customer needs, they would not return. Give the customer good service, and they would return. Milo had stats for the last five months, since their last performance appraisals: Alisha – 9.1%, Bryce – 5.3%, Charles – 6.2%, Esther – 8.2%, and Fred – 4.5%. Dave had told Milo that it would take a year for the preference measures to get into that target 8-10% range. Alisha and Esther had punched through a couple months early, both into the target range. Alisha had the highest numbers at 9.1% of her customers being return customers. Milo was proud of Alisha's recovery from the Patti Foster event, and of Dave's Subs as a whole, in showing support of Alisha the entire way through.

There was one last rate-based outcome measure that needed to come into play, that being time and attendance. While not explicitly a core measure, time and attendance was certainly a requirement to work at Dave's Subs. Dave had a pretty loose, rate-based policy. Show up to work. If you have to miss, find someone to cover your shift. If you can't, let Milo know. The number of uncovered days in the last year played out as follows: Alisha – 3 (excluding her two weeks of paid administrative leave), Bryce – 2, Charles – 6, Esther – 5, and Fred – 2. It was striking that the most reliable guy would have been Charles but for his five days tied to the state legislature sit in and tangle with the police officer.

Next, Milo looked at the project outcomes, tasks where artisans set out to produce a result on their own, and where they had primary control over the project's success or failure. The first project he thought about was the Memorial Day marketing campaign where Esther did an outstanding job on the actual flyers, but failed in only distributing half of them by the due date. The other big project, of course, was the mobile kitchen involving Bryce and Fred. Part system breakdown caused by a very poorly designed process, part at-risk behavior on both Bryce and Fred's part in choosing to continue handing out those warm, marginal subs. On the positive side, was Charles and Bryce's development of the website and their continued monitoring and responding to posts on review and social media sites. Dave's Subs was certainly reaping the benefits of their efforts in both tangible and intangible ways and had long ago begun paying them to stay after work as necessary to manage the monitoring and updates.

Finally, Milo pulled the events, the mishaps, things that happened that weren't aligned with the values of Dave's Subs or its customers, which had occurred over the past year. Events are generally rare. If events were going to mean anything in a person's body of work, Milo thought he needed to look back a bit farther than just the last six months. Here's what he had. There was, of course, the Patti Foster event. Alisha had made an error, but more importantly, she engaged in at-risk behavior when she didn't do the verbal check of the gluten-free roll. In Milo's observations, he'd seen all of his artisans drift away from the check. This was really on him to manage; if he was managing the check and discovered that people were choosing *not* to do the check, then he probably wouldn't have to worry about their next performance evaluation.

The next event that came to mind was the skateboarding incident involving Fred, Esther, Bryce, and Milo himself. Milo's friend called it reckless on Milo's part. Milo accepted that, given his risk monitor was firing, albeit mitigated by that other voice telling him to let the team have some fun. Because his risk monitor fired, he chose to call it at-risk behavior on the part of his three employees.

And there was that one day where both Fred and Bryce irritated a few customers, Bryce sending that elderly woman to the back of the line, Fred writing "wow" on the woman's receipt.

Looking at it all, Milo was a little surprised to see just how much data he had to work with in trying to fairly assess his sub artisans. Much more happened in his first year than he ever remembered happening in a year at store #1. Evaluating his own performance, Milo thought he could do much better than he did, but gave himself some grace in that it was his first year managing a store, as well as far exceeding Dave's expectations for operationalizing his letter to employees after the Patti Foster event.

Milo laid it out like the teacher he was, drawing upon an academic grading scale he'd sometimes use with his guitar students, and began grading each of his artisans, working hard to be consistent and not let grade inflation creep in. For Milo, an A really was an exemplary grade, a B meant you were above average, C said you were average and meeting expectations. While Milo didn't hand out any D's or F's to his current group of artisans, in his mind the D stood for "needs lots of improvement and is precariously perched on the employment bubble" and F meant failure, time to terminate.

When Milo was finished, the grades in his notebook looked like this:

ALISHA

CORE MEASURES:	75%
SUBS/RUSH	A
REPEAT CUSTOMERS	A
ADDITIONAL ITEMS:	25%
ATTENDANCE	B
VALUES-SUPPORTIVE BEHAVIORS	B
GOING ABOVE AND BEYOND	C
OVERALL GRADE:	A

Dave's Subs

Bryce

Core Measures:	75%
Subs/Rush	B
Repeat Customers	B
Additional Items:	25%
Attendance	A
Values-Supportive Behaviors	B
Going Above and Beyond	B
Overall Grade:	B

Charles

Core Measures:	75%
Subs/Rush	C
Repeat Customers	C
Additional Items:	25%
Attendance	C
Values-Supportive Behaviors	A
Going Above and Beyond	A
Overall Grade:	C

Esther

Core Measures:	75%
Subs/Rush	A
Repeat Customers	A
Additional Items:	25%
Attendance	C
Values-Supportive Behaviors	B
Going Above and Beyond	B
Overall Grade:	A

CORE MEASURES:	*75%*
SUBS/RUSH	C
REPEAT CUSTOMERS	C
ADDITIONAL ITEMS:	*25%*
ATTENDANCE	A
VALUES-SUPPORTIVE BEHAVIORS	B
GOING ABOVE AND BEYOND	C
OVERALL GRADE:	*C*

Milo liked what he'd created. He knew that corporate human resource departments would probably scoff at his back-of-the-napkin approach to assessing employee performance. He didn't have a formal employee tracking system nor did he have a lot of formal procedures guiding his way. He did hope that Dave's Subs would take what he'd done - a significant improvement, he knew, over his earlier "gut instinct" review, biased undoubtedly by recent events, good and bad, - expand it and implement a more formal assessment procedure for all stores.

In the meantime, Milo only had his five employees and what he had written down in his notebook – and performance appraisals to do. Milo wasn't out to be elegant, he just wanted to be right, to be just in his decisions around his employees. Ultimately, it was his decision about who was to be an artisan at Store #6. And it was his decision how to compensate them for the value they provided Dave's Subs. His employees could walk at any time, finding a better deal across town. It was his job to attract and retain good employees. It was his job to deliver what Dave needed from him in running his store.

Dave had authorized Milo to make adjustments to salaries based upon Milo's assessment of his artisans' work. There was no pool to distribute. Starting salaries were 25% over minimum wage. The maximum salary for a sub artisan was capped at 75% above minimum wage, and that space was largely reserved for artisans who could produce at 80 subs per rush, with greater than an eight percent preference score, and longevity with Dave's Subs.

Dave tended to give larger than industry salary hikes to counter the high turnover in the food service industry. Rarely did an employee last more than 3 years, even at Dave's. It was the nature of the restaurant business; most of Dave's employees were going to school, and Dave's was a way to support themselves on their way to somewhere else.

The higher than average raises allowed Dave to retain employees for a slightly longer period of time, though, and Dave found in his few short years that employees with a year or two of experience definitely outperformed employees in the first six months. Fast and friendly service was not as easy as it appeared, and if Dave found employees who could deliver, he wanted to make sure they were rewarded so that he'd keep them just as long as he could.

Dave had reviewed his thinking about wage increases with all of the managers; with that in mind, Milo set out to decide raises. And here is what he did:

ALISHA	$11.00/HR (30% ABOVE MINIMUM)
ESTHER	$11.00/HR (30% ABOVE MINIMUM)
BRYCE	$9.35/HR (10%)
CHARLES	$9.10/HR (7%)
FRED	$8.50/HR (NO RAISE)

It was not an easy decision for Milo. There was a wide distribution in their raises based primarily upon their performance against the core measures. If you were a top performer at Dave's Subs, you were above 80 subs per rush, and your return customer rate was above 8%. Alisha and Esther were the top performers; they received a significant bump on their way to the artisan maximum of 75% above minimum wage. Bryce's raise reflected his performance against core measures, while Charles' equivalent raise reflected the intangibles he brought to the store. Fred didn't receive a raise because his performance was marginal against the core measures, nor did he offer any real intangible benefits to Dave's Subs.

Milo spoke to each artisan. He described to them how he assessed their performance, and how he had decided their raises. Milo took their input, just as he did throughout the year. Performance reviews were special, though, as it gave Milo a formal time with each employee to talk about what was important to Dave's Subs, and for Milo to learn what was important to his artisans. They were all on their way somewhere else, but while they were at Dave's Subs, it was one of Milo's objectives to be a good employer. Three of the five reviews stood out, each for their own reason.

ALISHA

"It's been a tough year," said Milo.

"Yeah, quite frankly, I'm surprised I am still here at Dave's Subs to have a review," responded Alisha. "I didn't think I would survive what I did to Patti Foster."

"What *we* did to Patti Foster," Milo corrected her. "I share the responsibility for what happened to Ms. Foster. We've got a good system now. Everyone is working had to make sure that kind of event doesn't repeat itself."

Alisha just gave Milo a smile, grateful and not knowing what to say.

"Alisha, you know that you are one of our top two performers," said Milo. "Your core measures are great at 86 subs per rush, and at 9.1% repeat customers, you rate the highest. Those are excellent numbers. You embody fast and friendly service. And you do it safely, notwithstanding the Patti Foster event. I watch you make safe choices each and every day. And, importantly, I see you coach your fellow artisans. You're not going to be perfect, and we don't need you to be that. You're doing the right things. Keep up the great work!"

FRED

"Fred, I'm taking everyone through formal performance evaluations. We do it once a year."

"So where am I at?" asked Fred.

"You're making 62 Subs per rush, and your repeat customer preference measure is at 4.5%," said Milo.

"Sweet! I hit the minimum! And the repeat number? What is that? Let me think...roughly one out of 20 customers is a repeat customer? That's pretty good, isn't it?" asked Fred.

"No," said Milo, "it's really not. It's the lowest in the store. We'd like to have you above 8%. And we'd like to have you making 80 subs per rush."

"Crap. I thought I was doing well," said Fred.

"Fred, I've spoken to you about these measures throughout the year," said Milo. "This cannot be news to you."

"I get along with my fellow artisans. I get a few customers to laugh," said Fred.

"You do. You're fun to have around. And, you get a few complaints," said Milo. "Fred, you're not where you need to be. You're a bit risky in your tone with the customers, and you're not producing subs at the rate you should be able to. You're not receiving a raise because of the quality of the work product you're producing now. I need you to step up your game if you want to have a future here. I need you to be at 70 and 7, by the next quarter's numbers. It's a matter of hustling. I'll work with you, but this is going to come back to you."

"Milo you pay me $8.50 an hour to make subs," said Fred. "What do I get if I sprint like Alisha or Esther? I can see them hustle. And you're going to give me a raise to $9.00 if I hustle. Frankly, it's not worth it to me."

Milo was taken aback. He didn't quite know what to say to Fred. He didn't feel compelled to say that Alisha and Esther were at $11.00 an hour. He sat for a moment staring at Fred, an awkward silence between them.

"OK, Fred. I get it," said Milo. "You're not going to hustle to get to the 80 and 8, nor even to the 70 and 7."

"Nah...I just don't see the value. My cousin is a nighttime security guard making $13.00 an hour. I mean cushy job. He's not sprinting. He's reading a book, watching monitors," said Fred.

"Fred, I have to change the tenor of this conversation," said Milo. "We have customers lined up outside during most of our lunches. We need to serve them as fast as we can because they have only a limited time for lunch. It's that fast and friendly service thing. Fred, I need you to be at 70 subs per rush. If you choose not to get there, I don't think this is going to be the right place for you. I'm going to watch over the next two weeks. That's the timeframe I am going to give you to pick up your speed."

"OK, Milo. I'll see what I can do," said Fred.

The topic of the raise didn't even come up. Fred was resigned to make his $8.50 an hour, just tooling along. Milo saw no reason that Fred couldn't produce 70 subs per rush. Milo saw no physical limitation; this was simply about the effort that Fred was willing to put into his work. Fred pretty much confirmed that himself. Unsurprisingly, Milo left that performance review believing that Fred had only two more weeks at Dave' Subs.

CHARLES

"Charles, I want to thank you for being an artisan here at our store," said Milo.

"You're welcome," said Charles.

"We've talked throughout the year," said Milo. "You've 'tilted' a bit more toward production since our last conversation, and that has your core measures pointed the right way. You're doing about 63 subs per rush, and you're preference numbers are up to 6.2%. It's not the best, but those core measures are not the only thing I look at."

"Remind me again, what's the target?" asked Charles.

"Eighty subs per rush, a return customer score above 8%. Think '80 and 8,'" said Milo.

"Milo, I just don't think it's in me to do 80 subs per hour," said Charles. "Our Friday lunch rush is a holy terror. I simply can't keep up with your younger artisans, especially Alisha and Esther."

"Charles, I don't need you to," said Milo. "We come in all shapes and sizes, as they say. Not everyone is going to be able to sprint for 90 minutes like Esther or Alisha."

"I sure hope you take care of those two," Charles chuckled. "They are just delightful young ladies."

"Yes, they are. And they are taken care of," said Milo. "That said, I also want to take care of you. I want to make sure you are compensated for what you bring to the table. And I have a few ideas for that."

"Milo, I'm a retired school teacher. I'm here to get out of Beverly's hair. Other than that Friday lunch, it's pretty fun for me. I'm thankful for what I have," said Charles.

"I have a couple of suggestions to help get you where you need to be," said Milo. "First, I'd like to suggest a bit of a job share. I can try to keep you off of the Friday schedule if that helps. But when you do work a Friday, how about I swap stations with you from 11:30 – 1:00. Let me be the artisan, you can work food prep, and deal with any customer issues."

"Milo, why would you...?" asked Charles, his voice catching.

"Because you're a good guy to have on the bus," said Milo. "I value your experience, and your mentoring of me and your fellow artisans. During that crazy Friday rush, you're just in the wrong seat. I still like the hustle; remember, I was an artisan just a year ago! I think I can give Alisha and Esther a run for their money. It's for 90 minutes on Friday. We can just swap jobs for a bit."

"Why would you do that?" asked Charles.

"Because I want to honor what you do bring to the table. I have been learning this last year about being a manager. You know Dave and I have been working to make sense of Alisha's error. We said that Alisha was more than that one mistake, that she had a 'body of work' that mattered more. You, Charles, have a body of work that fits well with Dave's Subs. You're not the fastest. But you bring wisdom and experience to the table, that frankly, the rest of us are a little light on."

"You know, Milo, I left teaching because I didn't think I had anything left in my gas tank," said Charles. "My teenage students just wore me out. I knew it was time. Yet, after a year sitting around the house, I thought I could make a contribution. I just needed to do something different. I needed to feel of value. You just did that for me. Thank you."

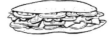

Milo left his first five performance evaluations feeling drained. Four of them were hopeful, one, Fred's, was an outright downer. Milo knew he could not tolerate Fred's unwillingness to hustle to meet the demands of the customers lined up every rush. Fred stood alone as the one guy who didn't seem to be trying. It was as if Fred made the bargained for exchange – pay me $8.50 an hour, and you get 62 subs per rush, nothing more, nothing less is what his attitude said.

The other artisans heard the message loud and clear. Every artisan had an idea of the production levels of their peers. Being an artisan was a physical job. To pay every artisan the same seemed like punishment for the top performers, who were clearly Esther and Alisha. Every one of the artisans had compassion for Charles; they could see that he hustled to the best of his ability. And Bryce, he was a solid performer. Everyone could see that he was doing the best he could and doing reasonably well by the core measure standards. But Fred's unwillingness to hustle had a very real impact on his fellow artisans and was creating a significant downward drag on morale at Dave's Subs. It was Milo's responsibility to address it.

WALKING THE STREETS

Milo was still bothered. Fred had posed a dilemma. In the moment, Milo was willing to tell Fred that he needed to get his sub production up to 70 subs per hour. Milo believed that Fred had it in him. With a little effort, Fred could be at 80 subs per rush, helping the store to meet the demands of its customers waiting in line during the lunchtime rush. What was bothering Milo was that Fred *did* meet the company minimums of 60 subs per rush. How could Milo take issue with an employee who was indeed meeting the minimum standard? Was it fair to ask more?

Nothing that Milo had explored over the past year had given him an answer to this question. Yet, for Alisha and Esther, it was a critical question. Why should they hustle when Fred was allowed to coast? Was a potential raise enough to reward the performers from those who chose to coast?

Choose to coast. That's where the problem lay, as far as Milo could see. Esther and Alisha had less issue with Charles – feeling somehow that 80 subs per rush wasn't in Charles to give. The problem was with a person who had the capacity to hustle, but chose not to.

Milo has a large extended family, and many of them live in nearby communities. Occasionally, as a family, they would go into Manhattan. Sometimes to see a show, sometimes to Central Park, other times to the more hip areas around Greenwich Village and Soho. It would be 20, sometimes 30, people walking as a group. And for Milo's father, Ernesto, it was a matter of keeping the herd moving along. All it took was one person to stop in a store, especially down in the Soho shopping district, before the entire group was brought to a halt. Milo could see the anxiety in his father. For Ernesto, out for a Sunday stroll meant a Sunday stroll – not the starts and stops of 20 independent people. For Ernesto, a stroll was meant to be continuous.

Milo and Isabel could quote what Ernesto would say, "Get a move on, those feet were meant for walking." Yet, Ernesto would not say it to his own mother and father, both of whom were in nearly 80. Nor would Ernesto say it to the little ones, the less-than-five year old crowd. Ernesto seemed to recognize their limitations. Ernesto kept his comments reserved for the teenagers and their able-bodied parents.

There was for Ernesto, a duty of family members to keep pace. Physical limitations due to age or disability, he recognized. But if you had the capacity to keep pace, it was your duty to do so. As long as the pace was reasonable, the duty was there. It was a duty owed to the family. It sprang from a set of set of shared family values, at least that's how Ernesto saw it. The family takes a Sunday stroll together, that means keeping up with the pace of the group.

Thinking about the family stroll helped Milo reconcile his thoughts around Fred. Yes, Fred met the minimums. But his obligations to the team did not end there. There was an additional duty owed to the team that itself came from the shared values of the team. At Dave's Subs, the team viewed that 90 minutes around the lunch hour as a sprint. Every team member had to hustle – within the capacity that each person brought to the job – to work through the line of customers. Charles hustling was different than Esther hustling – they had a different capacity.

Fred? He was choosing to coast, like the teenagers on the Alvarez Sunday stroll. Fred had 70 subs per rush in him, probably 80. And if he had it in him, he needed to produce. Produce, or let another person take his spot. This wasn't only a management view; the team shared it.

Everyone needed to work hard. In Alisha and Esther's views, it was Milo's job to help (and require) each team member work to their potential. Everyone had a different potential, and that was ok. It was the choice to coast, in a job that required hustle that rattled the rest of the team. It even bothered Charles, who himself was not producing subs at the fastest rate. Charles could see that Fred was coasting. Everyone knew it, and as long as Milo left it unaddressed, it was a sore spot for the rest of the team.

Fred needed to perform up to or near his potential. If he chose to coast, he increasingly became a cancer to the store's culture. Minimums or not, Fred needed to know he had a duty toward the team. Milo knew Fred had 70 subs per rush in him, and that's what Fred needed to produce. It was reasonable, and his fellow artisans demanded it. Just as Ernesto demanded hustle from his grandchildren.

TWO FINGERS

He was the last person Milo expected to see. Wild Bill himself walking through the front door of the store.

"Howdy, Milo," he said.

"So to what do I owe this pleasure?" Milo said in a slightly formal voice.

"I've been in town visiting my sister. Thought I'd stop by and see how you're doing," said Bill. "Got a few minutes to chat?"

It was the afternoon, the day winding down. "Of course, I do," said Milo.

They both sat down at a table at the front of the store. "Get you juice or some water?" said Milo.

"Nah, I'm still bloated from that lunch with my sister. Can't fit another thing in my belly," said Bill.

"So I been hearing good things about what you been doing over this last year. Figuring out how to build a strong culture of accountability here at the store?" asked Bill.

"Yeah, it's been a journey. Not an easy one. I do know a heck of a lot more now than I did when we last met, that's for sure. Getting better around system design – your coaching was great," said Milo.

"How's that artist of yours? The one who gave the wrong sub roll? She still with you?" said Bill.

"Yeah, Alisha is still with us. We call them "artisans,' Milo corrected Wild Bill. "She's actually one of my top performers."

"Oh, sorry about the name thing. That's great news," said Bill. He seemed genuinely pleased with Milo's progress and the news that Alisha had survived the Patti Foster storm. "So, are you watching for the drift we talked about?"

"Yes, I do. I even came up with a label for it. I call it 'at-risk behavior,' and I'm always on the lookout. Don't want another Patti Foster event," said Milo.

"So, can I ask?" said Bill pointing at an old injury on Milo's left hand.

There was a moment of awkward silence as Milo stared at his hand.

"I don't generally talk about it," said Milo. "I was in an automobile accident the day after my high school graduation. Another student from my high school, a year younger than me, ran a stop sign and blind-sided my car. I was lucky to have lived through it. I didn't have my seatbelt on. Got thrown around the car, my hand got caught on the sharp edge of a piece of window trim. Changed my life for sure," said Milo, subdued by the memory.

I'm very sorry to hear of that. How did it change your life, if I can ask?" said Bill.

"In high school, I was a pretty good musician. Ok on the piano, but pretty good on the guitar. I actually had a scholarship to NYU. It wasn't Juilliard, but NYU is pretty renowned for its music program. It was my way of getting into and paying for college. The accident screwed up those dreams," said Milo.

"Wow," said Bill. "So what happened to the guy who hit you?" said Bill.

Milo sat, again staring at his hand for a moment. Bill had the patience to let him drift a bit. "His name is Bobby Ray McClellan. He ran the light. It was a clear summer day, so there were really no extenuating circumstances. Bobby Ray was fiddling with his radio, trying to tune in to a new station, his head down as he approached the intersection. He told the police he didn't even see that the light was red. In a less than stellar investigation, the police report cited 'distraction' as a cause of Bobby Ray's running of the red light."

"And what happened to the guy?" asked Bill again.

"He got a ticket for negligent driving. His parents insurance covered the injury," said Milo. "I can remember being pretty upset by the police report. Distraction. That was what the police report said. Distraction. One guy's distraction cost me two fingers. It cost me my musical career," said Milo.

"Sorry for asking this, but did you forgive him?" asked Bill.

"I was 18 years old. I simply did not have the skills to forgive," said Milo.

"Interesting you were the one to have to deal with this lawyer and her gluten-filled sandwich," said Bill.

"Yeah, you're right," said Milo. "In this entire year, I haven't once gone back to Bobby Ray. That was the past for me. However I coped with it at the time, I've really left it in the past. Perhaps the Patti Foster event was meant to be a lesson for me."

"What do you mean?" asked Bill, already knowing where Milo was going, but just wanting him to say it.

"I've held a lot of internal, but unspoken and unaddressed anger toward Bobby Ray. I've seen him on the street a few times over the last 10 years. There was no way I was going to talk to him. The anger would just overcome me. And I'd like to think I am a pretty well balanced guy," said Milo.

Bill and Milo sat silent for a moment.

"You know, after this year, I can think differently about that event," said Milo. "But I am not sure whether it is acceptance or forgiveness that applies."

"What do you mean?" asked Bill.

"If we are indeed inescapably fallible human beings, then there seems nothing to forgive. We simply have to accept our mutual fallibility. Design better and better systems, but beyond that just accept the results we get."

"Yes, but this guy Bobby made a choice to focus on his radio instead of the intersection ahead," said Bill.

"I know. And I don't think for a moment that Bobby as a 17 year old was thinking he was risking my life. He wasn't reckless. Stupid, but not reckless," said Milo. "I guess if I forgive Bobby, it is to release him from the burden of the injury he'd caused."

"So is that justice? Or is that just letting him off the hook?' asked Bill.

"I guess that takes us back to Dave's Subs and Patti Foster. Would firing Alisha be the justice that Patti Foster needed?" asked Milo.

"In her mind, probably – and in the minds of a lot of other people as well. That's the problem you face, Milo," said Bill. "You can be accepting and forgiving inside Dave's Subs, but that doesn't change the world around you. We humans are pretty simple. Bad outcomes are caused by bad people. That's what we believe, no matter how irrational it is. And you aren't gonna change what the public believes," said Bill.

"You're probably right. But I gotta give credit to Dave for trying to do the right thing inside his own business," said Milo. "And believe that it can spread through our employees and their encounter with Dave's Subs."

"Indeed," said Wild Bill. "Indeed."

Closing the Books

It seemed to Milo there was one last conversation he needed to have with Dave, he had wanted to wait for two weeks, until he had the new numbers for Fred.

"Dave, I have to tell you, performance evaluations are really tough," said Milo.

"Why's that?" asked Dave.

"No matter how many great ones you have, they can get overshadowed by one bad one," said Milo.

"I didn't tell you that being a manager was going to be easy. It's a very tough job. It's particularly rewarding for some people. It's exhausting for others," said Milo.

"So can I tell you about the performance evaluations I just finished?" asked Milo.

"Sure, I'd love to hear. But first, I heard Wild Bill stopped by the store," said Dave.

"Yeah, its always interesting to see that guy," said Milo. "He asked about my fingers."

"Wild Bill has no filter, no inhibitions – if he's got a question, he'll ask," said Dave. "Perhaps that's what helps him be a consultant."

"You know, I haven't thought about my accident this entire year. Sorta blocked it out. It's been close to 15 years. But I do have to tell you that Patti Foster's event did help me resolve my anger toward the guy who hit me."

"How's that?" said Dave.

"It seems to me we spend too much time looking to blame after events, and a lot less time than we should preventing them in the first place," said Milo. "If we're gonna build a better world, we gotta learn from events…and then we need to move on."

"Nicely said. I'm glad you had the chance to catch up with Wild Bill. He can be a great mentor to us both," said Dave. "With that, how about them evaluations."

"I did them two weeks ago," said Milo. "Four of the five went really well. Alisha and Esther are still the stars at Store #6. I scored the artisans on a new scale I created, A-F like a teacher, with 75% of the overall score coming from the two core measures, and the remaining 25% coming from the intangibles. The intangibles included time and attendance, values-supportive decision-making, and going above and beyond job requirements. It may seem a little strange giving a grade to time and attendance and values-supportive decision-making. If an artisan is serving in an unsafe manner, or is rude to customers, that is more of a pass/fail kind of criteria, but that would only be if that were typical behavior for the artisan. Everyone can have a bad day, or just an impossible customer; that's why I gave a letter grade. Anyway, like I said Esther and Alisha were the stars."

"How did Bryce do?" asked Dave.

"Pretty well, he was right there in the middle of the pack. He's at 77 and 5.3 with the core measures."

"Good. I like Bryce. He's had a tough life, and I'm glad to see that we're a part of him making his way in a small way," said Dave. "I'm still hoping, however, that you can get him into that 80 and 8 range."

"Me too," said Milo. "Now its Charles and Fred that were the interesting ones."

"I might have guessed," said Dave.

"I'll start with Charles," said Milo. "He's a really good guy. You already know that I think very highly of him. He's helped me grow as a manager, and he just has such generosity watching out for his fellow artisans. Anyway, he's at 63 and 6.2. Not great against the core measures, but he goes above and beyond. He'll volunteer for anything I ask, and he'll coach me when he sees me drift as a manager."

"That's good," said Dave.

"I made a bit of a deal with Charles," said Milo. "Sorry I didn't get your approval first, but I think you'll be fine with my proposal. I committed to help Charles on the crazy Friday rush. I volunteered to switch with him for the 11:30 - 1:00 period on the Fridays he's scheduled. He can prep and run food, deal with customer issues, while I hustle as an artisan for 90 minutes. It helps him, and it helps the store...and I get to give Alisha and Esther a run for their money!"

"Ahhh...competitive are we? Are you sure this is something you want to do?" asked Dave.

"Yes, I am. Charles is a good guy. I want to keep him as an artisan. He's good for me, he's good for the other artisans, and he's good for Dave's Subs. And I don't mind. It actually keeps me in tune with being an artisan. Who knows?" said Milo. "I may come up with some system refinements that get us to 90 or 100 subs per rush."

"Hold on, dude!" said Dave, smiling. Your proposal sounds like a good deal. I'm impressed with the solution you've come up with to deal with a slower artisan. Now tell me about Fred."

"Yeah, onto Fred. Frankly, he just floored me," said Milo. "He's at 62 and 4.5. And he's content to be there. He actually said it was not worth whatever raise I could give him to get him to hustle to produce 80 subs per rush. He wasn't motivated to sprint. It was that simple for Fred."

"Hmmm…" said Dave. "Don't think I've ever heard that one before. People might have been thinking it, but nobody has ever been bold enough to actually say it. So whatcha' gonna do?" asked Dave, thinking he had a pretty clear idea of what he'd do given the same circumstances.

"Well, during the performance review, I encouraged him to see 70 subs per rush as a target," said Milo. "But when he told me he wasn't motivated to get there, I guess I was just flabbergasted. My tone changed - I think I was even shaking a bit - but I told him that I needed him to get to 70. I told him I would help where I thought I could, but that I thought it really was about a willingness to hustle and that was really up to him. I ended up putting him on notice. Told him that he had two weeks to get up to 70. If he wasn't motivated to get there, then this probably wasn't the right place for him."

"Right on!" blurted Dave. "You know, this isn't the same thing as Alisha's error. That was a human error. It sounds like Fred was making a choice not to hustle where Fred has it well within his capacity to get to 80 subs per rush, but just doesn't want to work that hard. 70 subs is a reasonable requirement. We've got customers standing in line. This is no place to have an employee who wants to coast along in first gear."

"Dave, that's exactly what I thought – and essentially what I told him when I put him on notice," said Milo.

"So where is he at now? Over the last two weeks?" asked Dave.

"Well, he's actually slowed down," said Milo. "My discussion with him appears to have been a de-motivator. He's averaged 56 subs per rush since our discussion."

"Damn, you gotta give him credit for holding his ground," said Dave.

"Yeah, and I meet with him tomorrow. He's gone," said Milo.

"Agreed. He's not someone we can afford on our team," said Dave.

It struck Milo as ironic that his journey led to this. He'd been asked to operationalize Dave's letter to the team. And his last conversation about it ended with firing an employee. It was clear to Milo that Dave never intended to toss out any form of employee accountability in writing his letter. Dave could see that if he fired Alisha, she was being fired for causing a horrible outcome. To Dave, that was unjust. Milo could fire her for making a mistake, or for drifting into an at-risk behavior, but that too would be firing her for simply being human. Humans make mistakes and they drift into at-risk behaviors – its part of being human.

The differences between Alisha and Fred were obvious. Fred was being fired for a decision to coast at his job. He had it in him to hustle, to produce 70 subs per rush. Would it be easy for Fred, who constitutionally was not somebody who enjoyed hustling? No. But Milo was not committing that being a sub artisan at Dave's Subs would be an easy job. In fact, Dave went out of his way to express to all of his prospective applicants just how hard a job it was, and what kind of a sprint it was to work a lunch rush.

Milo had come full circle, from Alisha to Fred. The workplace was a place of a bargained-for exchange. Dave's Subs could provide something to its artisans, and in return its artisans provided something to Dave's Subs. Just what each side should or could provide was the question for Milo. And, in the course of a year being a new manager, Milo thought his grasp on what it meant to be a good employee and what it meant to be a good employer had widened significantly.

Milo recalled Aristotle's quote: "At his best, man is the noblest of all animals." For Milo, justice, how we hold each other accountable, was at the core of what made us human, the core of what gave us a shot at nobility.

Dave was a noble man, having decided not to terminate his employees for making a mistake. And Milo's search to operationalize Dave's decision had made Milo a better manager, a better man. Noble even!

Learning Points

Written for the Manager of People

Chapter 1

The Day It Happened

Alisha delivers the wrong roll. Patti Foster is injured. Dave and Milo are left to make sense of it.

Bad events will happen. It's the nature of business; it's the nature of life.

When bad events do occur in the workplace, we're left as managers to decide how to respond. Was our system designed to create the right outcomes? Did our employees do what they needed to do? Did we as managers do what we needed to do? How are we all held to account for our contribution?

Chapter 2

Decision Time

Dave decides that Alisha will not be fired. Dave writes the letter – "I will not fire an employee simply because they have made a human mistake."

Perfection cannot be the expectation, neither at the system level, nor at the level of an individual employee.

We are inescapably fallible human beings. No matter how we are pieced together as a collection of human beings, we will inevitably produce undesired results. As they say, it's not a matter of "if," it's only a matter of "when."

We can strive for perfection. It's a lofty goal. But an aspiration is different than holding perfection out as an employment expectation. Perfection as an expectation is wrong. It's not right for employee, and it's not the path to producing better outcomes.

Chapter 3

Not So Easy

Milo begins his journey to figure out what accountability will look like at Dave's Subs. From the start, he's got a hunch it's a more complex than Dave's letter portrays. His first task: to differentiate choices and errors.

Milo sees there's difference a between human errors (mistakes) and the choices we make along the way. Every adverse event seems to include human error. Beside or behind those errors, however, are choices, coming from both of Kahneman's System 1 (subconscious) and System 2 (conscious) brain. Those choices play an important role in undesired outcomes.

From texting while driving on the road, to knowingly violating rules at work, we humans create hazards through our choices, often without any recognition of the hazard we create.

CHAPTER 4

YELP

Charles and Bryce voluntarily build the website in order to help attract customers back to Dave's Subs.

As a manager, it's easy to focus on the downside – those things our employees do that don't measure up to expectations. We shouldn't lose sight of the upside, the outcomes we hired the employee to produce, and those times where our employees have gone above and beyond. Extra effort, like that shown by Charles and Bryce, has an important place within the body of work.

CHAPTER 5

PABLO'S

Dave visits Pablo's restaurant out at the track. Hand written orders. Runners to and from the kitchen. It's the worst system design he's ever seen.

Employees live within the context of a "system." It's how we designed the workplace; it's how we designed specific tasks. Sometimes we design it well. Sometimes, we don't.

We cannot expect our employees to overcome bad system design. Design a bad system and it will lead to an increased rate of human error, and an increased rate of at-risk behavior.

System design is half of the equation – design good systems to get good results.

CHAPTER 6

WILD BILL

Wild Bill comes in to assess the operation. He suggests the coaster as an additional safety strategy. He also questions the long-term effectiveness of other strategies, such as the out-loud check.

Every manager is a system designer at some level. Learning to design well, in recognition of our employees' inescapable fallibility and propensity to drift, will make the difference in any effort to produce good results.

Well-designed systems will have barriers to prevent errors, recovery to detect and correct errors made earlier in the process, and redundancy to make a system more tolerant of error and at-risk behavior.

CHAPTER 7

NICE TRY

Bryce tells a slow-ordering customer to go to the back of the line. Fred writes "wow" on a customer's receipt. Milo's got to quickly address them both.

Values. - Service. Safety. Friendliness.

They are abstract ideas. What it means to be unfriendly, what it means to be overly friendly – these are not easy to identify. Yet, we know them through our shared values. We are all accountable for our conduct in the world. Beyond the rules we create for our employees will be a set of shared values – coming from society, the organization, perhaps even the local group. It's our duty to conform our conduct to that set of shared values.

And it's our task as managers to hold our employees accountable for conduct inconsistent with those shared values.

CHAPTER 8

FINDING THE HIDDEN APP

Milo's playing games with his two brains when he's alerted to the boy running into the street to retrieve a soccer ball. Milo discovers his risk monitor. It stands watch to the world around him, alerting him to the presence of danger.

We all have a risk monitor. Yet, through life experience, everyone's risk monitor works differently. You see hazards that others do not see, and others see hazards not visible to you.

Our ability as humans to align our conduct to a shared set of values is directly tied to how well our risk monitors function. With no risk monitor, no filter, everything looks reasonable. With a highly tuned risk monitor, we humans can make good choices in an increasingly complex world.

Chapter 9

Wally's Wieners

Bryce and Fred take the mobile kitchen out to a park grand opening. A human error leads to a missing power cable. Heat takes an increasing toll on sub sandwiches. Bryce and Fred make a number of on-the-spot decisions.

As a manager, you're tasked with observing the conduct of your employees. There will be times, like that which faced Milo, where it's hard to see the wisdom in your employees' choices.

Ask yourself: Did their risk monitor fired? Did they not see the hazard? Did they see the hazard but misinterpret its significance? Did they see the hazard yet ignore what they saw as a significant risk?

We all make weird choices in the moment that will look pretty straightforward with the benefit of hindsight. Ask yourself as a manager, what would you and others have done in the same circumstance?

CHAPTER 10

JUSTIFIED

Ester's job was to make subs. She had a line of customers ahead of her. Yet, Esther left her workstation to give aid to the victim of an auto accident.

It was the right thing to do. There is no procedure to tell us what is the right thing to do. There is no procedure that tells us when to violate a duty or rule. Yet, we all see the justification.

We humans live with multiple overlapping obligations. And, on top of that, we occasionally have the opportunity to help someone along the way.

Breach of a duty is sometimes warranted. And it will be our shared values that help us decide when that's the case.

CHAPTER 11

HORIZONTAL BOARDING

Milo looks on as Bryce and Esther convince Fred to skateboard in the store. Fred falls. Milo's golf buddy, John, calls it "reckless."

Reckless. It's the conscious disregard of a substantial and unjustifiable risk. It is a term describing when the risk monitor alerts the conscious (system 2) brain to a significant and unjustifiable risk, and then that conscious brain chooses to ignore the threat.

You as a manager will face circumstances where it appears clear that your employee was knowingly taking a risk, generally out of self-interest, that brings hazard to others. The employee does not mean to harm, yet they choose to gamble with others in pursuit of their own interest.

Chapter 12

Nice Guys Finish Last

Charles in not producing to the core measure – 60 subs per rush. Milo has a crucial conversation with Charles. Charles reacts well.

We hire employees to produce outcomes – either rate-based or project-based outcomes. As a manager, we work to help our employees meet the expectations. We can be role models. We can mentor. And, we can coach. Sitting down with an employee, talking to them about what steps they can take to meet expectations. Helping our employees produce good results. It's at the core of being a good manager.

CHAPTER 13

UNCLE JULIO

Uncle Julio meant no harm to others when he drove intoxicated, yet he gambled with the lives of those around him. Milo found himself struggling to separate "recklessness" from words like theft, arson, and murder. Those involved an intention to harm. Uncle Julio was a nice guy – he meant no harm.

Employees will occasionally intend harm – it is seemingly just part of our human condition. Recklessness is different – it's the choice to gamble. When a person sees the risk, without intending harm, but chooses to gamble, to pursuit their interest while simultaneously endangering others, then they have acted recklessly. And reckless is a place where disciplinary sanction can have impact.

CHAPTER 14

PANTOPHOBIA

Lucy labels Charlie Brown. Pantophobia – the fear of fear itself. A nice label, but what is Charlie Brown to do with it? And that is where Milo found himself. He's developing labels but finding it hard to pull it together into a working model.

Human error, at-risk behavior, and reckless behavior all have independent meaning. They are labels to guide our actions as managers. Being able to differentiate a human error from a reckless choice is important in determining what we might do with system design, and how we might engage the employee's behavior within that system.

Chapter 15

None of Your Business

Charles gets arrested for elbowing a police officer in the face. It's off duty conduct, yet it causes Charles to miss a week of work. It gets Milo to think about the role of off-hours conduct.

As a manager, we're occasionally stuck with evaluating the off-duty conduct of our employees. It's a slippery area – and there is no universal answer. Perhaps it is best to simply ask if the off-hours conduct is relevant to the employee's job? Charles' protesting seems not to be. A banker who is a thief in her off hours may be relevant. A million dollar football player engaging in physically risky, off-the-field activities, such as BASE jumping, surely is.

Chapter 16

Slicing Beef

An artisan cuts her hand on a meat slicer. And that's the extent of the investigation. Milo pushes Dave to believe there is more.

Bad outcomes occasionally happen. When they do, you as a manager should push behind the bad outcome to the systems and behaviors that led to the bad outcome. Behind every error and every at-risk behavior is an explanation. Look for it. What about the employee's work system contributed to the event? What choices did the employee make? Why did they make them? Only then will you have the information needed to learn from the event.

CHAPTER 17

FLIGHT

Denzel Washington plays an intoxicated pilot in *Flight*. The aircraft crashes, but not because of his intoxication. No harm, no foul?

It may be the most important lesson in this book. No harm, no foul is a lousy business strategy. As a leader you create good outcomes by designing good systems around your employees, and then helping them make good choices in those systems. Employees need to be accountable for what they can control (i.e., their choices). Turning a blind eye to risky choices simply because there was no harm is a good recipe for eventually getting you the undesired results you are actually trying to prevent.

CHAPTER 18

THE GULF

Milo struggles in the gulf between human error and reckless behavior. Milo can see that humans make risky choices without seeing them as excessively risky. They're recurring choices – many just looking like habits. They are not human error. Nor are they reckless.

Milo labels them "at-risk." And he quickly concludes they are a central figure in the task of managing employees.

Human beings drift. They see the real value in cutting corners, yet they often do not see the risk. So they slowly drift into riskier and riskier choices. As a manager you address the system contribution to at-risk behavior, and you try to coach the employee back into safe choices. Being an effective manager means that you are working to help eliminate the at-risk behavioral drift of your employees.

CHAPTER 19

TREBLE MEANS TRIPLE

Potato chips taken up to his daughter's room. Milo and Isabel see the risk, his daughter does not. Dave sees that natural consequence (ants in his daughter's room) just doesn't seem to be the right solution. Milo realizes that sanction (disciplinary action in the workplace) is really artificial danger created by those in authority.

You will use the tool of disciplinary sanction as a manager. It's a tool to shape behavior. It is artificial danger that can be detected by an employee, causing them to make a different calculated choice.

Termination is not artificial danger - it is simply the parting of ways. It is the threat of termination that is designed to change a person's choices. And it works.

CHAPTER 20

AYE, AYE COACH

Milo watches his music student's football coach. And, for the first time, he sees his model in action. Console the human error, coach the at-risk behavior, and sanction the reckless behavior – all independent of the actual outcome.

It's the core of the model introduced in this book. Console the human error, coach the at-risk behavior, and sanction the reckless behavior – all independent of the actual outcome. Don't wait for harm to occur and then whack whoever was involved. Be an actively engaged manager, especially around detecting and correcting the at-risk behaviors of your team.

Chapter 21

Educating Dave

Milo gives his first report to Dave. It's focused on events – the body of work stuff will wait for the second report.

Console the human error, coach the at-risk behavior, and sanction the reckless behavior – all independent of the actual outcome. That was the core of Milo's report. Design good work systems around your employees. Learn from things that do not go as planned. And, console the human error, coach the at-risk behavior, and sanction the reckless behavior – all independent of the actual outcome.

CHAPTER 22

THE PIT

Milo was feeling bad about his contribution to the Patti Foster event. The focus was on Alisha, yet Milo had to own his part as her manager. Milo apologizes to Alisha.

Everyone plays his or her role – manager and employee. Think of it as "shared accountability." As a manager, your job is to set up the system in which your employees work, and to help them be successful in that system. That includes the task of identifying and correcting at-risk behaviors before they lead to harm.

CHAPTER 23

POTPOURRI

Dave gathers his managers to review events, to look for common threads. Milo points out that they're all just looking at outcomes – missing the data that describes why these undesired outcomes are occurring.

It's good as a manager to know what's happening – especially the undesired outcomes. It's even better to know *why* they are occurring. A learning culture means employees are reporting events, and both managers and team members are learning from them. Your search for causes should get you back to systems and choices that lead to undesired outcomes. And, in the case of risky choices, your search should look for the reasons your employees are making those choices.

CHAPTER 24

UPSETTING ESTHER

Esther learns that, in another store, raises were distributed based upon performance. Milo admits to the "peanut-butter" spread – every employee getting the same raise. It's got Esther challenging Milo, and its got Milo searching for answers.

We hire employees to produce outcomes – whether it's subs per rush as an artisan, or it's patients cared for as a doctor. In many jobs, employees do have the opportunity to differentiate themselves. The amount of hustle we put into our work will be directly tied to the outcomes we produce. And when that's the nature of the job, it's reasonable for employees to expect that their hard work gets recognized.

CHAPTER 25

MOVIE NIGHT, AGAIN

Milo watches his favorite movie – *It's a Wonderful Life.* George Bailey leads a life of service, yet one mistake for which he is responsible starts to unravel his life. Milo starts thinking about the "body of work."

As inescapably fallible employees, we're destined to have our bad days. Those days need not define us as employees. There is a broader picture we can see of each employee if we step back to look at their entire body of work.

As a manager, you should view single events with caution – they often tell you very little about your employee. A broader and more inclusive picture can give you a richer understanding upon which to evaluate the performance of your employees.

CHAPTER 26

AN INJURY-FREE WORKPLACE

Dave suggests to Milo that they reward teams that can go three months without an injury. Milo takes issue with the strategy.

It seems like something to aspire to – perfection for a period of time. Yet, it has its downside. It rewards human beings for being lucky.

To justly measure outcomes, both the numerator (events) and denominator (opportunities) must be statistically significant. When we're down to one versus zero events, we're essentially evaluating luck. It's better to focus on more statistically valid measure – like audits of behavioral choices. Are your employees making safe choices? That's the better measure.

CHAPTER 27

THE CORE MEASURE

Milo turns to thinking of the core measures – subs per rush, and rate of repeat customers. With all his focus on events, Milo has to think through what he owes his employees around the core production requirements and goals.

Outcomes represent the core measure of every job. Is our employee doing what we hired them to do? We can create expectations by specifying minimum requirements. And we can set specific targets for reward when performance goes well above the minimums.

Following procedures and respecting values are what we ask of employees along the way. Yet, they are not why we hired our employees. We hire employees to produce.

CHAPTER 28

HOME CONSTRUCTION

Milo attempts to build his daughters a playhouse, without instructions. It does not go well. It turned Milo's attention to the role of instructions and rules.

We provide instructions to employees when they need particular knowledge for "how" to perform a task.

We impose rules when we want to constrain our employees, either by prohibiting specific conduct (the don't do's), or by proscribing the way it is be performed (the how to's). It is within rules that we create expectations, with sanction for non-compliance attached as artificial danger.

CHAPTER 29

WHY ALISHA?

Milo gets his first look at the store's customer preference measures. And he finds that Alisha is at the top of the list. Yet, without minimums, he finds himself at loss for how to use the data.

As managers, it is our job to measure the performance of our team members. Some of those measures will have minimum expectations, such as time and attendance. Some will not, such as Dave's preference measures. All measures have relevance to an employee's body of work.

CHAPTER 30

UMBRELLA'S INDEED

Esther helps Milo with a marketing program. It is a project-based outcome. Esther hits the mark on some parts, missed it on others. Milo begins to see the difference between rate-based outcomes and project outcomes.

Rate-based outcome measures focus on a statistically significant group of outcomes, like subs per rush.

Project-based outcomes are those single outcomes we set out to create – from building something, to running a marketing campaign. We measure these in a different way. Too few to be statistically significant on their own, we break down the outcome into parts: on time, on budget, in compliance. In project outcomes, we measure an employee's ability to create a single result.

CHAPTER 31

CULTURE OR BUST

Milo talks to Lou Garuda, a long time Navy man. Lou and Milo talk about culture – and what it means to have a culture of accountability.

Most employees hire on at a company within a framework of a simple transaction – physical/mental work in exchange for a salary. Being a good employee, however, means more than simply producing the desire outcomes. It means following rules; it means aligning one's choices to the shared values of the organization.

Chapter 32

Showing Off

Dave takes his managerial team to lunch, where the waiter memorizes the orders of the seven participants. Milo sees it as at-risk behavior. It's here that Milo first explains his model to fellow store managers.

Human error. At-risk behavior. Reckless behavior. Outcomes. Procedures. Values.

They are the concepts of Milo's culture of accountability. They are the words, all having meaning, that can make sense of what we see in the workplace, from how we set expectations, to how we think of breach.

CHAPTER 33

THE BODY OF WORK

Milo has his second conversation with Dave. This time it's about the body of work.

It's the body of work that gives us the best picture of our employees.

We articulate a mission. We talk to our teams about the values we need to protect. We give them instructions, and educate them on the rules.

Then, we watch. Outcomes are measured. Events pop up along the way. As best we can, we integrate these outcomes and events into a bigger picture we call the body of work. It's the bigger, more statistically valid view of our employees. It's by reference to that picture that we make the big decisions, like promotions and raises.

CHAPTER 34

LA GRANDE JATTE

Isabel takes Milo and the girls to the Metropolitan Museum of Art to see Seurat's *La Grande Jatte*. Milo's daughter, Emily, blurts out, "It's just a bunch of dots!" The excursion helps Milo answer a nagging question about the body of work.

Emily was right. It's all dots - or in the employment context, all outcomes and events. Even abstract ideas like friendliness come down to our recall of either negative or positive events. We cannot see friendliness directly; we see it through events.

Sometimes a single event overshadows the other dots making up the picture of an employee. Lance Armstrong's admission of illegal drug use is but one example.

In the end, the more we can see, the better our assessment of one's body of work.

CHAPTER 35

MAKING CHOICES

Milo conducts his first formal performance reviews. He's painted a picture of each employee, and with that picture determined the raise he's going to offer each artisan. In discussions with each, he finds Fred unwilling to step up.

Managers must conduct performance reviews. It's that broader look, beyond what can be see in an instant of time. It's through the review that we might make the bigger decisions, from salary changes, to promotions or demotions.

CHAPTER 36

WALKING THE STREETS

Milo's discouraged by Fred's unwillingness to step up. Fred is making minimums, yet his lack of hustle is impacting the morale of the better performers. In his search for answers, Milo finds a duty owed the team. And, in the process, puts Fred on notice.

Most of us work on teams. Our employer might create specific outcome expectations, yet there is a duty owed the team that exists independent of the minimums. It's tied to the notion of pulling one's own weight, to work to one's potential. It's a duty owed to peers, and to the organization. It's tied to our shared values. It's why fellow artisans have compassion for Charles, yet contempt for Fred. Charles is working to his potential while Fred is coasting.

As a manager, you'll evaluate whether an employee is doing what they can. If not, perhaps your team is not the place for them.

Chapter 37

Two Fingers

Wild Bill stops by the store. He asks about Milo's two missing fingers. Milo describes his own tragedy, and his own emotional struggle with the guy who caused it.

Acceptance and forgiveness. They are not easy concepts. We often expect perfection from others. It doesn't get us the outcomes we desire; yet it seems to be the societal standard.

As a manager, if you follow the human error, at-risk, reckless model, you'll be at odds with how the greater culture sees accountability. No harm, no foul – until someone is hurt, then it's "how bad was the outcome, who do we blame?" Being a good manager, building a culture of accountability, might mean you will be at odds with what others see as the optimal path.

Chapter 38

Closing the Books

Milo has one last conversation with Dave. He's put Fred on notice. Someone was about to be fired, and it was not inconsistent with Dave's letter to his employees.

A culture of accountability means that we are all accountable for what we can contribute to the team. We're given natural talents, and we're given the free will to make good choices. Yes, we're inescapably fallible humans beings. That said, we can and should be held to account for our contribution as an employee. We just need to do it in a way that is open, fair, and just. That's the right brand of accountability.

AUTHOR'S NOTE

Author's Note

It's written as a story. A fiction. There is no Dave's Subs. There is no Dave. There is no Milo. I wrote this as a story to make the points stick. Hopefully, you've found it an enjoyable read.

At this point, you should think you know Alisha, Bryce, Charles, Milo, Dave, Esther, and Fred just as you know the characters in your favorite movie or television show. Let their stories be a guide to you. You can manage a group of engineers, a group of doctors, a group of accountants, a group of salespeople – no matter who you manage, you will see these characters in your life. Having worked in the food service industry, having worked with astronauts and doctors, I can attest to the fact that we are all human beings. We pursue happiness. We love liberty. We protect our property. We are altruistic, and we are self-serving. We are inescapably fallible. We are human.

Being a manager of inescapably fallible human beings is no easy task. My hat goes off to those managers who are already great at what they do – and there are quite a number of you I've met out there.

For every person asked to manage, there is the uneasy task of holding team members accountable for their conduct. It is an uneasy task because there is no "right" answer to this task. Not everyone is a doctor, not everyone a gymnast, not everyone a craftsman, but we are all judges. It's in our DNA to judge each other. And there should be little doubt that it's deeply engrained in organized society, from the criminal law, to teachers grading papers, from rules and penalties on the sports field, to employment law practices.

Without judgment, there is anarchy. Holding each other accountable for our conduct is an essential part of what binds us together. As our society has advanced, however, we've found a few ways to drift from an optimal course: we create unreasonable expectations of perfection, and then we play no harm, no foul. We turn a blind eye to risky behaviors, that is, until someone is hurt. Then, and only then, our usual response is to whack the person who caused harm.

What's described in this book, what's first crafted by Dave and fleshed out by Milo, is what high consequence industries like aviation and health care have come to know as a Just Culture. To create better outcomes, those industries have sought out different systems of justice to be more just, so that they could produce better outcomes.

For healthcare especially, where most recent estimates suggest that the US healthcare system alone kills more than 440,000 people each year, it has been imperative that different organizational create different cultures. Hospitals have moved away from historically punitive cultures where physicians, nurses, pharmacists, and other staff report only what they cannot hide. They've worked hard to create learning cultures where employees are encouraged to raise their hands when they see hazards, and when they themselves have made mistakes. And hospitals have learned to investigate at greater depth, to understand why human errors occur, and why at-risk behaviors develop.

The change in culture began with words like "non-punitive culture," but almost everyone quickly realized it was not a system without artificial danger that we sought, but instead a system of workplace justice that used the threat of disciplinary sanction in a more limited way, in a manner that held employees accountable for their choices. It was a more "just" culture.

I started my journey toward Just Culture back in 1970s when I took my first job at an ice cream parlor. Knowing the crazy things we high schoolers did with ice cream, I can first hand attest to the fact that there is a need for punitive sanction, simply for the safety of the ice cream eating public.

I then moved onto work at the then largest bar in the state of Arizona, right there on the edge of the campus of Arizona State University. Engineering student by day, bartender by night. It is at Minder Binders (that's what the bar was called), serving a group of often-intoxicated college students, where I honed my customer service and public speaking skills. I knew then it was the most fun I would have at a job, while simultaneously having, perhaps, the least social value.

Upon graduating with a degree in systems engineering, I moved to Seattle so that I could live out my desire to be an aircraft designer. Technically, I was less of a designer, more of an analyst. My job was not to design the aircraft, but instead to think about how it might fail, to think about how we would avoid the catastrophic failure sequence that would take out the aircraft. I was not on a computer designing parts, I was instead looking at failure sequences, and how the failure of any of six million parts on an aircraft could lead to disaster. It was rewarding work. Life was good.

Until I read a book entitled *Blind Trust* written by John Nance. It changed the course of my life forever. In *Blind Trust*, John Nance told the story of the growth of the science of human factors at the National Transportation Safety Board. That was all it took. I was hooked. Working on aircraft was fun, but I wanted more of a challenge. I wanted to design systems where humans themselves were the principle components in the system. It added an intriguing layer of complexity. Physical parts could fail, just like humans. Yet, humans added the additional layer of free will. Parts either did or didn't do what you told them to do. If they weren't doing it, it was some form of mechanical failure or code failure. Humans though, they would do what they were told, they would fail (the human error), and then they would also just go and do something totally different than they were asked (the at-risk and reckless behaviors). For me it was just too interesting to pass up.

At Boeing I had the unique opportunity to start a human factors group. Our mission was to reduce the likelihood that technicians working on an aircraft just might do something to take out our aircraft and its very valuable human cargo. I was learning the science of human factors at work, being mentored by some of the best experimental psychologists and human factors practitioners in the world. It was the opportunity of a lifetime. Off hours, I was pursuing a juris doctor. My mentors with PhDs in cognitive psychology didn't quite get the purpose of a law degree, but there was something pointing me in that direction that I just could not ignore. I would learn that there is indeed a reason that most congressmen are attorneys; law school is a great course of study on the design of human systems.

I eventually worked my way to starting Outcome Engenuity, a small firm created to help organizations produce better outcomes. That is, how do organizations get the most out of their collection of human beings? Through OE, I was getting the chance to take the skills I learned in designing aircraft with millions of physical components, to the design of organizations with thousands of human components. From managing a small business, to working with, and sometimes, inside large corporations, I can again tell you that we all share very similar characteristics in our human fallibility.

To a large extent, the tools for managing human fallibility are the same, from restaurants to hospitals, airlines to small manufacturing enterprises. It's part systems engineering, and it's part psychology. I still meet leaders today who believe only pilots can manage pilots, only physicians can manage physicians, only engineers can manage engineers. It's a terribly antiquated idea that's not very helpful for the organization, or for those being managed. There really is little a doctor learns in medical school that prepares them to lead a group of doctors, and in particular, that very narrow piece of managing human fallibility.

The management of human fallibility, the steering of another human being's choices, is still more art than science. Yet, with the great work done by researchers like Daniel Kahneman, with great advances in the fields of systems engineering, cognitive psychology, behavioral economics, we are seeing this part of management becoming more science, and a little less art. We've learned a lot, and with that learning, it has for me opened the door to seeing our justice system, at large, and that practiced inside organizations, as being behind the times. What we've learned about human reliability should be shaping a different system of workplace accountability, that abandons notions of perfect human performance as a predicate for good results, and one that stops turning a blind eye to risky behaviors simply because no harm was caused. No harm, no foul must go. Expectations of individual perfection, and system perfection, must go as well. Every manager should consider the merits of the commitment that Dave made to his team. By re-examining what it means to hold employees accountable, we will get better results, for our customers and the employees we manage.

Being a manager is a great job. It's hard work, but rewarding. It is my hope that *Dave's Subs* can be of help to you. Let's work to build an even more aspirational and effective workplace.

With thanks,

DAVID MARX

www.DavesSubs.com

CPSIA information can be obtained at www.ICGtesting.com
Printed in the USA
LVOW11*2051220815

450960LV00001BA/1/P